ENVIRONMENTAL CHEMISTRY:

AIR AND WATER POLLUTION

H. Stephen Stoker
Spencer L. Seager

Department of Chemistry
Weber State College

Scott, Foresman and Company
Glenview, Illinois London

Picture Acknowledgments

We wish to thank the agencies listed below for photographs used on the front cover and the part opener pages—

Part One: Air Pollution Control District, Information and Education Division, County of Los Angeles

Part Two: United States Department of the Interior, Fish and Wildlife Service

Library of Congress Catalog Card Number 73-184964.

Printed in the United States of America.
Regional Offices of Scott, Foresman and Company are located in Dallas, Oakland, N.J., Palo Alto, and Tucker, Ga.

Preface

The decade of the 1960s is known to some as the space decade. Undoubtedly the 1970s will similarly be known as the environmental, ecological, or pollution decade, for it is in this decade that environmental pollution has become a popular cause for concern. Prior to this time, individual voices of warning were heard, but only recently have large numbers of people begun to listen and take action.

Much of the material spoken and written about environmental pollution has been presented with great emotion from a position firmly on one side or the other of the issues. The author of a recent instructor's guide for a chemistry textbook found it difficult to recommend "responsible current books" as references to the text chapter dealing with the environment. As he put it, "too many adopt an exaggerated position."

Some scientists have made dramatic but probably exaggerated statements with respect to the immediate seriousness of pollution problems. These frightening pronouncements were pounced upon by the mass media and widely disseminated to the public. Predictably, public emotion quickly rose. The emotional surge probably reached a maximum during 1970. Hopefully, a period of less emotional, sober assessment will follow from which a more realistic picture of the pollution problem, its dangers and solutions, will emerge.

This book was written with that hope in mind. We have attempted to stand back and take an objective look at the problems of air and water pollution. Our main focus has been on the chemistry and chemical compounds involved, but some overlap into other scientific disciplines was unavoidable. We have included the latest information available. Much of the data contained in tables and charts came from U.S. Government documents and, although dated in the late 1960s, it does represent the latest and most up-to-date information available.

We have tried to present an unbiased look at our subject, but surely our feelings come through in some statements. In spite of our more or less neutral position, we do not want to imply that pollution is not a serious problem, nor that we are unconcerned about it. On the contrary, we are convinced that the pollution problem is huge and very serious, and our concern about it is profound. We feel, however, that most of our acute environmental problems can be solved with technology now available. More than technology is needed. The attitudes of people must be changed. Is the public willing to pay the price for clean air and water? Many people believe or act as if they believe that they can enjoy a clean environment while someone else pays the bills. The cost of realizing even a moderate improvement in the pollution problem will be in the billions of dollars and must be borne by everyone.

Man can survive as a species without cleaning up the environment, but the quality (and length) of our lives will suffer. Man has survived on the surface of the moon, an environment much more hostile than the most polluted one on earth. However, the quality of life on the moon left much to be desired (helmets, bulky suits, oxygen tanks, and so forth). Our technology can keep us alive, but our children might look through the face windows of their oxygen helmets into a tidal pool and see, not teeming life, but only polluted, poisonous water covered with an oil slick.

From this point forward, you will find the writing to be much more neutral and objective. It is our hope that you will be provided with information that will aid you in deciding for yourself what your feeling and actions will be concerning environmental pollution problems.

The supplementary readings listed at the end of each chapter are provided for the further expansion of the areas under discussion. They are drawn from two main sources, scientific journals and U.S. Government documents.

The journal articles pertain to recent developments and are mainly selected from the following journals: *Scientific American*, *Science*, *Chemical and Engineering News*, and *Environmental Science and Technology*. These journals are quite readable for the average student.

Government documents contain a wealth of information in the area of pollution. Although seldom used by students, they are available at an increasing number of schools. Most of them are written at about the same level as this text, and many of the figures and tables have been taken from such documents. We encourage you to engage in further reading from this source.

H. S. S.
S. L. S.
Department of Chemistry
Weber State College
Ogden, Utah

Contents

PART ONE AIR POLLUTION

1 Air Pollution—General Considerations 2

2 Carbon Monoxide 8

3 Oxides of Nitrogen 25

4 Hydrocarbons and Photochemical Oxidants 37

5 Sulfur Oxides 52

6 Particulates 65

7 Temperature Inversions and the Greenhouse Effect 83

PART TWO WATER POLLUTION

8 Water Pollution—General Considerations 90

9 Mercury 119

10 Lead 131

11 Detergents 142

12 Synthetic Organic Insecticides 152

13 Oil 168

14 Waste Water Treatment 178

Index 185

PART ONE

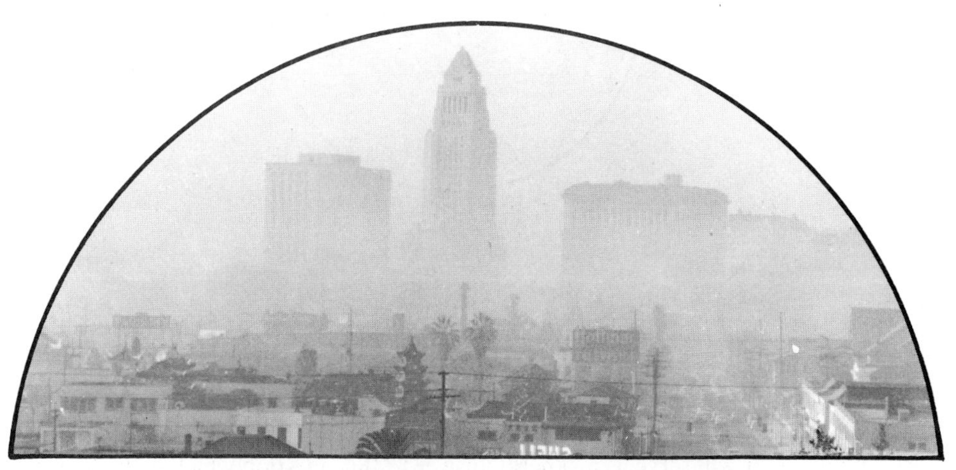

AIR POLLUTION

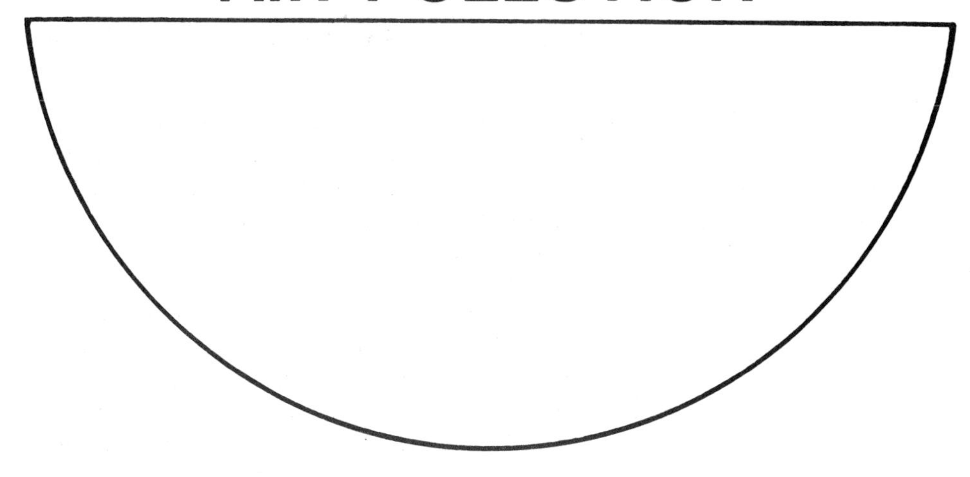

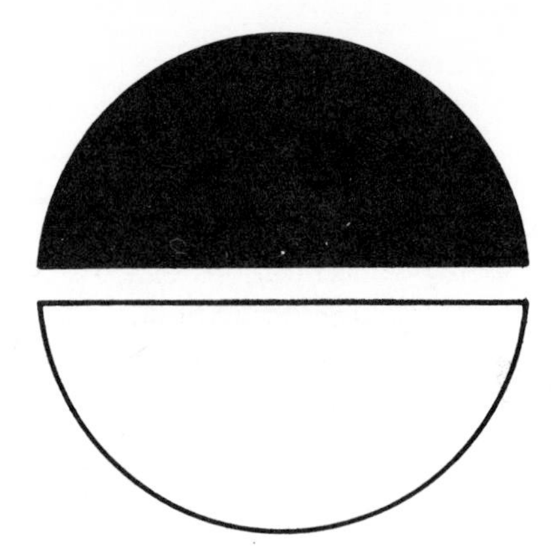

Chapter 1

Air Pollution–General Considerations

What is meant by the term *air pollution?* A comparison of unpolluted and polluted air will serve as a general answer to this question which is the logical starting point for any study of air pollution.

Unpolluted vs. Polluted Air—A Comparison

Air is a loosely defined term used to describe the mixture of gases that exists in a relatively thin layer around the earth. The composition of this mixture is not absolutely constant. Components showing the largest concentration variability are water (H_2O in vapor form) and carbon dioxide (CO_2). The amount of water vapor in air varies between values of a few tenths of 1% and 5 or 6% depending on the weather and temperature.

The concentration of CO_2 is always low, with a value usually of about three hundredths of 1% (0.03%). This concentration is increased somewhat (giving a total still measured in hundredths of 1%) in the vicinity of CO_2-producing activities such as vegetation undergoing decay, fossil fuels burning, or people breathing in a confined space. Relatively low concentrations are found over fields of growing vegetation or in air that has recently passed over the ocean. These low values result because of the absorption of CO_2 by plants during photosynthesis and the solubility of CO_2 in water. The effect of either variation on overall CO_2 concentrations in air is minimal because of the small amounts involved.

The composition of dry air, from which absolutely all water vapor has been removed, is found to be virtually constant over the entire world. The composition of clean, dry air collected near sea level is given in Table 1-1. All components which make up at least 0.0001% of the total volume are listed.

Two units are used in specifying concentrations: *percent by volume* is the volume of the specific component contained in 100 volumes of air, while *parts per million* (ppm) represents the volume of the specific component contained in 1 million volumes of air. Both units are used, but parts per million is especially useful when very low concentrations, common in pollution work, are being expressed. Notice that concentrations expressed as ppm are merely 10,000 times the volume percentage. In addition to the components listed, trace amounts (less than 1 ppm) of other gases are also found.

TABLE 1-1 COMPOSITION OF CLEAN, DRY AIR

GASEOUS COMPONENT	FORMULA	VOLUME PERCENTAGE	PARTS PER MILLION
Nitrogen	N_2	78.08	780,800
Oxygen	O_2	20.95	209,500
Argon	Ar	0.934	9,340
Carbon dioxide	CO_2	0.0314	314
Neon	Ne	0.00182	18
Helium	He	0.000524	5
Methane	CH_4	0.0002	2
Krypton	Kr	0.000114	1

Data for volume percentage selected from *Chemical and Engineering News* 44:20A (March 28, 1966).

Air is never found completely clean in nature. Such gases as sulfur dioxide (SO_2), hydrogen sulfide (H_2S), and carbon monoxide (CO) are continually released into the air as by-products of such natural occurrences as volcanic activity, vegetation decay, and forest fires. In addition, tiny particles of solids or liquids are distributed throughout the air by winds, volcanic explosions, and other similar natural disturbances.

Added to these "natural pollutants" are substances resulting from the activities of man. It is estimated that at least 200 million tons of man-made pollutants now enter the air each year in the United States. This amounts to about 1 ton per person annually, or between 5 and 6 lbs. per person daily. It is interesting to wonder what each of us would do with his daily share if it were delivered to the doorstep along with the morning milk and paper.

This yearly total of 200 million tons seems like a massive amount of material until it is realized that 3×10^{15} tons of air is present over the continental United States at any one time. If all 200 million tons of pollutants were distributed uniformly in this huge air mass, the concentration of pollutants would be less than 0.1 ppm by weight, as shown by the following calculation:

$$\frac{2 \times 10^8 \text{ tons pollutant}}{3 \times 10^{15} \text{ tons air}} = \frac{1 \text{ ton pollutant}}{1.5 \times 10^7 \text{ tons air}} = \frac{1 \text{ ton pollutant}}{15 \text{ million tons air}} = \begin{array}{c}0.067 \text{ ppm} \\ \text{(by weight)}\end{array}$$

Anyone experienced in the delights of inhaling polluted air knows that something must be wrong with the reasoning behind this calculation. The major error, of course, is the assumption that all the air over the United States at any one time is available to dilute the pollutants: the fact is that there is very little atmospheric diffusion of surface air beyond an altitude of 10,000 to 12,000 feet above ground level, and, in fact, many pollutants never rise beyond 2000 feet. Geologic and man-made barriers often limit lateral air movement as well, and they greatly decrease the mixing and diluting effects.

Thus, the reasons for the well-known buildup of pollutants beyond trace-level concentrations become apparent. Pollutant concentrations of 50–100 ppm have been observed but are not common (yet). However, concentrations in the 10–50 ppm range are not unusual.

Types of Air Pollutants—Sources and Importance

Five types of substances, known as primary pollutants, account for more than 90% of the nationwide air pollution. The five are:

1. Carbon monoxide (CO)
2. Nitrogen oxides (NO_x)
3. Hydrocarbons (HC)
4. Sulfur oxides (SO_x)
5. Particulates (part.)

Each of the five will be the topic for a detailed discussion in the following chapters. However, before these details are discussed, some general considerations are of interest. Two questions frequently asked about air pollution are: (a) *which type of source puts the largest amount of pollutant into the air?* and (b) *which single atmospheric pollutant is present in the largest amount?* The answers to these important questions provide an overall perspective of the seriousness and extent of air pollution.

TABLE 1-2 PRIMARY POLLUTANT SOURCES AND AMOUNTS (MILLIONS OF TONS/YEAR), 1968

POLLUTANT SOURCE	WEIGHT OF POLLUTANT PRODUCED					TOTAL WEIGHT OF POLLUTANT PRODUCED BY EACH SOURCE
	CO	NO_x	HC	SO_x	Part.	
Transportation	63.8	8.1	16.6	0.8	1.2	90.5
Fuel combustion (stationary sources)	1.9	10.0	0.7	24.4	8.9	45.9
Industrial processes	9.7	0.2	4.6	7.3	7.5	29.3
Solid waste disposal	7.8	0.6	1.6	0.1	1.1	11.2
Miscellaneous	16.9	1.7	8.5	0.6	9.6	37.3
Total weight of each pollutant produced	100.1	20.6	32.0	33.2	28.3	214.2

Adapted from U.S. Dept. of Health, Education, and Welfare, *Nationwide Inventory of Air Pollutant Emissions—1968*, p. 3.

The major sources and amounts of each primary pollutant are summarized in Table 1-2. According to this information, transportation is the main source of air pollution. This conclusion is reached simply by noting the 90.5 million tons of total pollutants produced per year by transportation and comparing it to totals from other sources. Carbon monoxide is the major individual pollutant, with a tonnage nearly twice as great as all other pollutants together. Thus, CO and transportation are often the first items mentioned when air pollution is discussed.

Evaluation of pollutants and sources solely in terms of tonnage has one serious drawback: it fails to take into consideration the possibility that one pollutant might be much more harmful or dangerous than another. Some attempts have been made to take into account such possibilities by assigning weighting factors to each pollutant. The greater the effect of a pollutant on the total environment, the larger the value of the assigned weighting factor. The weighting factors used in one approach, based on proposed air quality standards for California, are summarized in Table 1-3. The weighting factors in this case are the relative toxicities of the pollutants.

TABLE 1-3 POLLUTANT WEIGHTING FACTORS

POLLUTANT	TOLERANCE LEVELS ppm	$\mu g/m^3$	RELATIVE TOXICITY (WEIGHTING FACTOR)
CO	32.0	40,000	1.00
HC		19,300	2.07
SO_x	0.50	1,430	28.0
NO_x	0.25	514	77.8
Part.		375	106.7

Adapted from *Journal of the Air Pollution Control Association* 20:658 (1970).

A new concentration unit has been introduced in Table 1-3. This unit, *micrograms per cubic meter,* is a mass of pollutant per volume of air and is discussed near the end of this chapter.

The weighting factors of Table 1-3 are not exact, and conclusions reached by using them are probably best thought of as qualitative rather than quantitative. Nevertheless, they do provide a more reasonable indication of the air pollution problem than the oversimplified approach based entirely on total masses of pollutants.

Applying the weighting factors of Table 1-3 to the data of Table 1-2, the mass of each pollutant is multiplied by the appropriate weighting factor. The result is an adjusted mass of pollutant. These adjusted masses are then used to arrive at summation totals for each pollutant and source. Table 1-4 shows a comparison between the two methods (mass basis and weighted mass basis). All numbers are given as a percentage of the total.

TABLE 1-4 TOTAL EMISSIONS BY SOURCE—MASS VS. WEIGHTED MASS BASIS

POLLUTANT SOURCE	PERCENTAGE OF TOTAL EMISSIONS	
	MASS BASIS	WEIGHTED MASS BASIS
Transportation	42.2	15.4
Fuel combustion (stationary sources)	21.4	42.2
Industrial processes	13.7	18.1
Solid waste disposal	5.3	3.1
Miscellaneous	17.4	21.1

Conclusions based on the weighted mass calculations are somewhat different from those based only on total masses of pollutants. Transportation (mainly automobiles), the traditional villain of air pollution, becomes only the third most serious polluter when weighted values are used, and stationary combustion sources take over the number one position.

Even though these new conclusions must be considered as qualitative, they demonstrate that the pollution problem can and should be looked at from more than one point of view.

Units of Measurement

Concentrations of air pollutants are most often expressed in one of two ways. One of these, parts per million, is based on volume measurements and represents the volume of pollutant contained in 1 million volumes of air. The volumes of pollutant and air are determined at a standard temperature and pressure of 25°C (77°F) and 760 torr (atmospheric pressure at sea level) respectively.

The second way of expressing concentrations relates the mass of pollutant to the volume of air containing it. The unit often used is micrograms per cubic meter ($\mu g/m^3$), where one microgram is equal to 10^{-6} grams. In heavily polluted areas, milligrams (10^{-3} grams) per cubic meter are used in order to avoid using large numbers. A milligram is 1000 times larger than a microgram, so a concentration of 10,000 $\mu g/m^3$ becomes 10 mg/m^3.

Suggestions for Further Reading

Journal Articles

1. Babcock, L. R., Jr. 1970. A combined pollution index for measurement of total air pollution. *Journal of the Air Pollution Control Association* 20:653–59.

2. Lave, L. B., and Seskin, E. P. 1970. Air pollution and human health. *Science* 169:723–33.
3. O'Sullivan, D. A. 1970. Air Pollution. *Chemical and Engineering News* 48 (no. 24):38–58.
4. Atmospheric surveillance: the current state of air monitoring technology. 1971. *Environmental Science and Technology* 5:678–84.

Government Documents

1. U.S. Dept. of Health, Education, and Welfare. 1970. *Nationwide inventory of air pollution emissions, 1968.*

Chapter 2

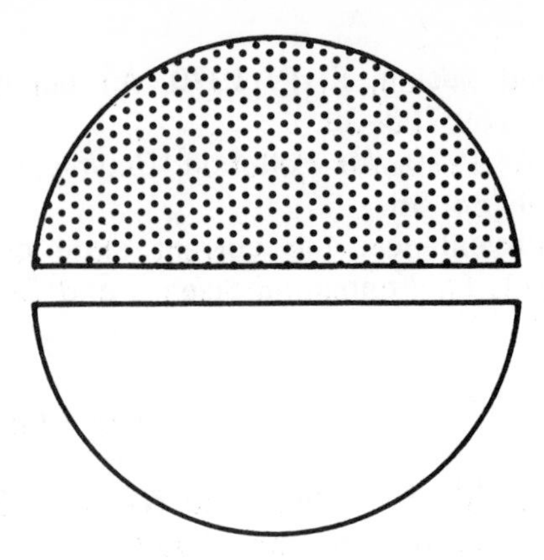

Carbon Monoxide

Basic Chemical Reactions

Carbon monoxide (CO), a colorless, odorless, and tasteless compound, is a gas at all temperatures above −192°C (−314°F). It is 96.5% as heavy as air and is not appreciably soluble in water. The formation of CO is generally the result of one of the following three processes:

1. Incomplete combustion of carbon or carbon-containing compounds occurs. This process takes place when the available oxygen is less than the amount required for complete combustion in which carbon dioxide (CO_2) is the product.
2. A high temperature reaction takes place between CO_2 and carbon-containing materials.
3. At high temperatures, CO_2 dissociates into CO and O.

The details of these processes include most of the chemistry of carbon monoxide important in pollution studies.

Process 1: The formation of carbon oxides is a simple process only when pure carbon and oxygen are the reactants. As it occurs during the combustion of carbon-containing material in air, the process is complicated and involves a series of reactions. Despite the complexity, certain general principles concerning the reactions are known.

In simplified terms, the combustion of carbon in fuel proceeds by way of the following steps:

$$2C + O_2 \rightarrow 2CO \qquad \text{(eq. 2-1)}$$

$$2CO + O_2 \rightarrow 2CO_2 \qquad \text{(eq. 2-2)}$$

The first reaction goes about 10 times faster than the second, so CO is an intermediate in the overall combustion reaction and can show up as an end product if insufficient O_2 is present to complete the second reaction. CO may be an end product even with sufficient O_2 present in the combustion mixture if the fuel and air are poorly mixed. Poor mixing leads to localized areas of oxygen deficiency in the air-fuel mixture.

The relationship between CO production and available oxygen (as measured by air-fuel ratio) is illustrated by Fig. 2-1, in which the CO production of three internal combustion engines is plotted versus the air-fuel ratio. The effect of low oxygen content on CO production is quite apparent.

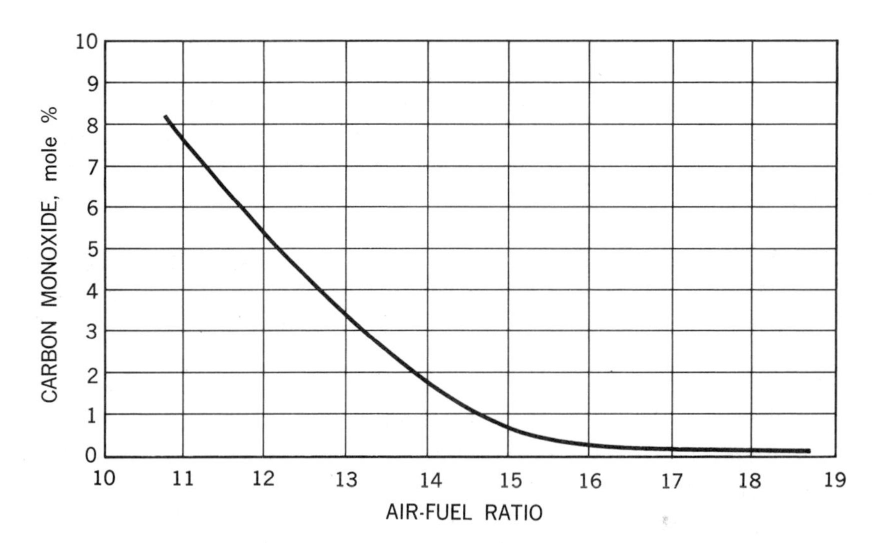

FIGURE 2-1 EFFECT OF AIR-FUEL RATIO ON EXHAUST GAS CARBON MONOXIDE CONCENTRATION FROM THREE TEST ENGINES

Redrawn from U.S. Dept. of Health, Education, and Welfare, *Air Quality Criteria for Carbon Monoxide*, p. 3-2.

Process 2: The reaction involved in this process is

$$CO_2 + C \rightarrow 2CO \qquad \text{(eq. 2-3)}$$

This reaction takes place readily at the elevated temperatures common in many industrial devices such as blast furnaces. The CO produced in this way is beneficial and necessary in certain applications, as in the blast furnace, where it acts as a reducing agent in the production of iron from iron oxide ores. However, some CO may escape into the atmosphere and act as a pollutant.

Process 3: Under appropriate conditions, a reaction in which sufficient oxygen is available for complete combustion may still behave as a source of CO. This is caused by a high temperature dissociation of CO_2 into CO and O.

Carbon dioxide and CO exist in a high temperature equilibrium situation as given by the equation

$$CO_2 \rightleftharpoons CO + O \qquad \text{(eq. 2-4)}$$

Higher temperatures favor the production of CO and O. For example, 1% dissociation of CO_2 into CO and O occurs at 1745°C (2960°F), and 5% occurs at 1940°C (3495°F).

If an equilibrium mixture at some high temperature is suddenly cooled, the CO present persists in the resulting cooled mixture because of the long time required to establish a new equilibrium at the low temperature.

Sources of CO Pollution

A number of geophysical and biological processes are known in which CO is produced. The processes include volcanic action, natural gas emission, electrical discharge during storms, seed germination and seedling growth, and marsh-gas production. The contribution of CO to urban atmospheres by these sources is thought to be relatively small.

The impact of CO released into the atmosphere as a result of man's activities is far from negligible, with more than 100 million tons released annually in the United States. Much of this amount is the result of various types of combustion processes as shown in Table 2-1.

Transportation contributes more CO than any other main category, and gasoline-powered motor vehicles contribute more than any other single source. Other forms of transportation contribute less, at least in part, because of the smaller number of vehicles involved.

The miscellaneous category is the second worst source of CO: this main category includes forest and structural fires, and deliberate agricultural and waste coal burning. Some statistics make the magnitude of this source apparent: in 1966, nearly 4.6 million acres of forest were destroyed by wild ("unprescribed") forest fires, and over 600,000 acres of National Park lands were burned by controlled ("prescribed") fires. The National Fire Protection Association reports that more than 1 million buildings are attacked by fire annually.

Agricultural burning, the largest contributor in the miscellaneous category, is a controlled burning of forest debris, crop residues, brush, weeds, and other vegetation. Such controlled burning is done for numerous reasons, such as the control of vegetation, insects, or other organisms harmful to desirable crops; the minimizing of fire hazards; the reduction of the volume of waste materials; and the clearing and improvement of land.

The main category of industrial processes is the third largest contributor of CO to the air and is the last with which we shall deal in detail. The two largest single contributors in this category are from the iron and steel industry. Major contributions also come from the petroleum and paper industries.

Carbon monoxide is generated during several of the operations used in iron and steel production. These operations are the beneficiating of ore (im-

TABLE 2-1 NATIONWIDE CARBON MONOXIDE EMISSIONS, 1968

SOURCE	EMISSIONS IN 10^6 TONS/YEAR			PERCENTAGE OF TOTAL		
Transportation	63.8			63.8		
Motor vehicles		59.2			59.2	
Gasoline fueled			59.0			59.0
Diesel fueled			0.2			0.2
Aircraft		2.4			2.4	
Railroads		0.1			0.1	
Vessels		0.3			0.3	
Nonhighway use of motor fuels		1.8			1.8	
Fuel combustion—stationary sources	1.9			1.9		
Coal		0.8			0.8	
Fuel oil		0.1			0.1	
Natural gas		N[a]			N	
Wood		1.0			1.0	
Industrial processes	9.7			9.6		
Iron foundries		3.6			3.6	
Blast furnace and sintering plants		2.4			2.4	
Petroleum refineries		2.2			2.2	
Kraft pulp paper mills		0.8			0.8	
Other		0.7			0.6	
Solid waste disposal	7.8			7.8		
Incineration		0.8			0.8	
Open burning		3.4			3.4	
Conical burners		3.6			3.6	
Miscellaneous	16.9			16.9		
Forest fires		7.2			7.2	
Structural fires		0.2			0.2	
Coal refuse burning		1.2			1.2	
Agricultural burning		8.3			8.3	
Total	100.1			100.0		

[a]N = Negligible.

Data compiled from U.S. Dept. of Health, Education, and Welfare, *Nationwide Inventory of Air Pollutant Emissions—1968*, p. 4, and *Control Techniques for Carbon Monoxide Emissions from Stationary Sources*, p. 2-2.

proving chemical and physical properties), blast furnace production of metallic iron, the basic oxygen, open hearth and electric furnace production of steel, and the casting operations performed in foundries. The greatest emission of CO takes place in the first and last of these processes. In the other two, gases containing CO are cleaned and used as fuel in the process itself.

The process of beneficiating ores is done in sintering plants. The ore is first ground to a fine powder, then the impurities and iron oxide are separated from one another by a magnetic process. After this improvement in chemical properties is completed, the powdered iron oxide is mixed with powdered coke (carbon), and the mixture is burned. As the coke burns, enough heat is generated to sinter (a sort of welding process) the small oxide particles into larger, more easily handled particles, and CO is generated and usually vented into the atmosphere.

The primary source of CO in the iron foundry is the cupola, or vessel in which iron is melted. Alternate charges of metals, coke, and limestone ($CaCO_3$) are placed on top of a burning coke bed contained in the cupola. The heat generated by the process melts the metal, which is then drawn off and cast. Again, CO is a by-product of the burning coke, and unless proper emission controls are used, it is vented into the atmosphere.

A process of regenerating catalysts is mainly responsible for CO emissions from the petroleum industry. In order to manufacture maximum quantities of marketable products from crude petroleum, it is the practice to subject the petroleum to one or more of the processes known as cracking, reforming, isomerization, alkylation, and polymerization. During these processes, the structures of petroleum molecules are tailored to fit the needs of the consumer. The use of catalysts makes it possible to carry out these reactions more efficiently and at lower temperatures than is otherwise possible. Most of the catalysts are used in the form of solid beads, pellets, or powders with large surface areas. The catalyst comes in contact with petroleum during the reactions and, after some use, becomes coated with carbon. The carbon must be removed to restore the activity of the catalyst. The conditions of temperature and air supply used during this reactivation cause CO to form. Catalysts used in cracking processes require frequent reactivation and are the largest source of CO in the group.

The wood pulp and paper industries, although often implicated in water pollution, also contribute to air pollution. Carbon monoxide is a by-product of a furnace operation in which valuable chemicals and heat energy are recovered from black liquor, a substance produced in the wood digestion process. In addition, some CO is produced in lime kilns used to regenerate lime from calcium carbonate.

The Fate of Atmospheric CO

The vast amount of CO dumped into the atmosphere annually is of concern because of the possible increase in atmospheric CO levels. Enough CO is put into the air each year, as a result of man's activities, to double its concentration in the ambient (surrounding) worldwide atmosphere every 4–5 years. The actual yearly increase in ambient worldwide CO concentration is known to be much less than that expected on the basis of annual discharges into the atmosphere.

The natural mechanism by which CO is removed from the air has been the subject of intense research. Some recent findings of this work are:

1. Atmospheric reactions are much too slow to account for substantial CO removal. The rate of the reaction $2CO + O_2 \rightarrow 2CO_2$ in the lower atmosphere has been found to be great enough to remove only 0.1% of the available CO for each hour of sunlight (sunlight is necessary in the reaction). On the basis of this rate, CO in the atmosphere would have an average lifetime of 3.5 months. This process cannot account for the observed slow increase in atmospheric CO.
2. Oceans have been shown to be sources of the gas.
3. Green plants grown under sterile conditions are unable to remove CO from the atmosphere.
4. Some microorganisms common to soil remove CO very rapidly from ambient air. A potting soil sample weighing 2.8 kilograms completely eliminated, in 3 hours, all CO from test atmospheres containing 120 ppm CO. Ordinary sod showed the same ability. Potting soil lost the ability to remove CO from the atmosphere when it was sterilized. Of 200 organisms isolated from the soil and cultured, 16 fungi have been found to be active in the removal of CO.

Thus, the major mechanism by which CO is removed from the atmosphere involves a natural soil sink that is dependent upon particular soil microorganisms for its operation.

Concentration and Distribution of CO

It is estimated that the soil sink in the United States alone has the capacity to remove more than 500 million tons of CO per year, which is 5 times the annual U.S. discharge into the atmosphere. Despite this large capability for removing the pollutant, CO at significant concentrations is still found in the atmosphere. The primary reason is that CO and the soil sink are not distributed uniformly. In fact, the largest CO producing areas of the country often have the least amount of soil sink available.

Because the automobile is the largest single source of CO pollutant (59.2%), highly populated urban areas show the highest ambient concentrations of CO. Within such communities the concentration of CO follows a regular daily pattern clearly related to human activities. These daily concentrations of CO correlate well with traffic volume: the highest correlations and the highest CO levels are found in areas of heavy vehicular traffic. Daily concentration patterns show little variation with the day of the week except for weekends. The weekday concentrations are higher than those recorded on Saturdays, which in turn are higher than those on Sundays. Figures 2-2 and 2-3 are examples of measurements illustrating the correlations discussed above.

The ambient air concentration of CO at any specific location is determined by the rate of emission into the atmosphere and the rates of dispersion and removal. In urban areas, the rate of removal by the soil sink is quite low and the other two factors become most important.

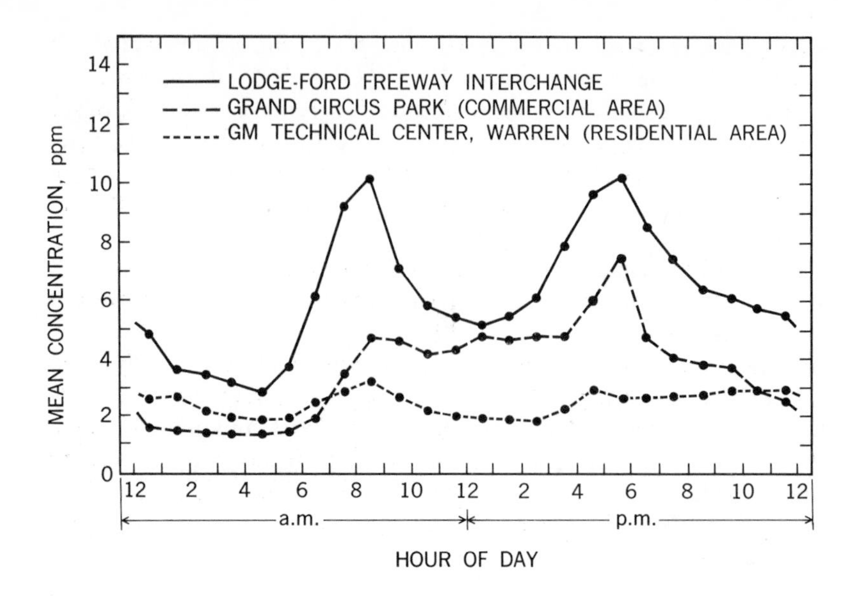

FIGURE 2-2 DAILY VARIATION OF CARBON MONOXIDE LEVELS ON WEEKDAYS IN DETROIT

Redrawn from U.S. Dept. of Health, Education, and Welfare, *Air Quality Criteria for Carbon Monoxide*, p. 6-2.

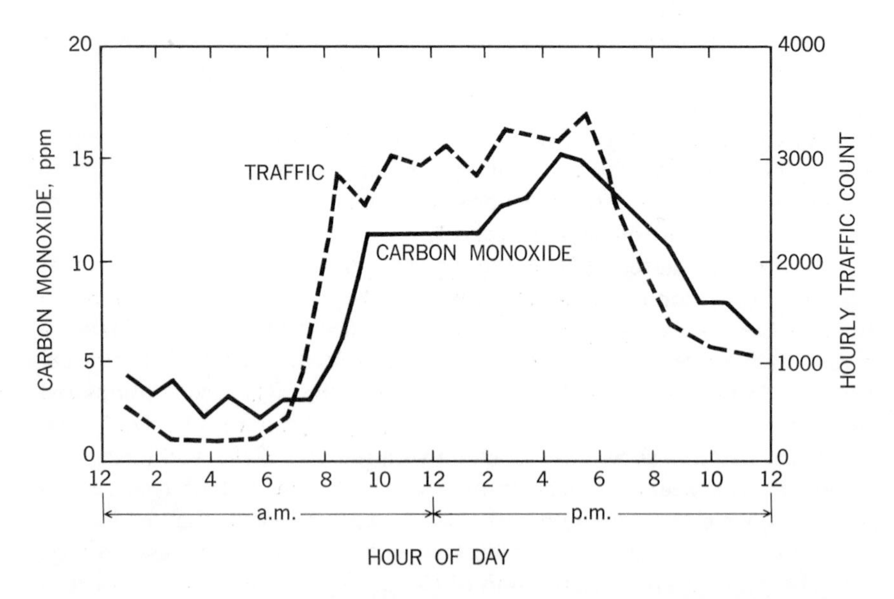

FIGURE 2-3 HOURLY AVERAGE CARBON MONOXIDE CONCENTRATION AND TRAFFIC COUNT IN MID-TOWN MANHATTAN

Redrawn from U.S. Dept. of Health, Education, and Welfare, *Air Quality Criteria for Carbon Monoxide*, p. 6-4.

The rate of dispersion is directly dependent upon the meteorological factors of wind speed and direction, air turbulance, and atmospheric stability. In large cities, even though turbulence is created by moving autos and air flow over and around buildings, prolonged periods of air stagnation occur which lead to inadequate dispersion and a consequent increase in ambient air CO concentrations.

Numerous studies have been done concerning CO concentrations in polluted air. In these studies concentrations are usually quoted on the basis of 8-hour averages. The 8-hour period is used because the body absorbs and desorbs CO slowly, and at low levels of atmospheric CO, 4–12 hours are required for an equilibrium to be established between the concentration of CO compounds in the body (mainly carboxyhemoglobin, COHb) and the average CO concentration of the inhaled air. Table 2-2 contains the results of measurements taken at continuous air monitoring stations throughout the United States. Data from many cities are included in each average value given. The values from each city included in the averages of the table are themselves averages over an 8-hour period. The numbers in the first column represent the average concentration for an 8-hour period exceeded at 5% of the reporting sites. This gives an indication of the maximum concentrations that occur, since only the most highly polluted sites are included. The numbers of the second column represent the average concentration for an 8-hour period exceeded by 50% of the reporting sites. This is a rough measurement of the median concentrations.

The average citizen is not subjected to 8-hour exposures of CO concentrations given for the first two locations of Table 2-2. However, cab and bus

TABLE 2-2 EIGHT-HOUR AVERAGE CO CONCENTRATIONS (ppm)

LOCATION	8-HR. MAXIMUM VALUE EXCEEDED AT 5% OF SITES	8-HR. MAXIMUM VALUE EXCEEDED AT 50% OF SITES
Inside vehicles in downtown traffic	115	70
Inside vehicles on expressways	75	50
Commercial areas	40	17
Residential areas	23	16
Background in relatively clean, unpolluted air	0.025 to 1.0 ppm	

Data selected from U.S. Dept. of Health, Education, and Welfare, *Air Quality Criteria for Carbon Monoxide*, p. 6-22.

drivers and traffic policemen could certainly be exposed to CO at such high levels. Table 2-2 indicates that the CO concentration encountered in heavy traffic is about 3 times that in commercial areas and 5 times that in residential areas. This fact has probably been suspected for years by the frequent user of crowded downtown highways.

The percentage of the time during which CO concentrations exceed specific levels is given in Table 2-3 for a number of cities. Again the data are for 8-hour average values of CO concentration.

TABLE 2-3 PERCENTAGE OF TIME DURING WHICH CO CONCENTRATION EXCEEDS SPECIFIC LEVELS, (1962–1967)

	% OF TIME CO CONCENTRATION EXCEEDED 10 ppm	% OF TIME CO CONCENTRATION EXCEEDED 50 ppm
Chicago	21	12
Cincinnati	8	5
Denver	12	7
Los Angeles	15	10
Philadelphia	12	7
St. Louis	10	6
San Francisco	8	5
Washington, D.C.	8	4

Data selected from U.S. Dept. of Health, Education, and Welfare, *Air Quality Criteria for Carbon Monoxide*, pp. 6-6, 6-7.

Effects of CO on plants

No detrimental effects have been detected in higher plants subjected to exposures of CO for 1–3 weeks at concentration levels up to 100 ppm. Nitrogen fixation ability of free-living bacteria was inhibited by a 35-hour exposure to CO levels of 2000 ppm. The nitrogen fixation ability of bacteria living in clover roots was inhibited after a 1-month exposure to a 100 ppm CO concentration. Since CO levels rarely reach 100 ppm, even for short periods of time, significant impact on vegetation and associated microorganisms seems unlikely at present.

Effects of CO on Humans

It is well-documented that exposure of humans to high concentrations of CO can result in death, but the effects of exposure to low levels (100 ppm or less) are just now becoming known. This concentration range is the important one where air pollution is concerned because ambient CO levels are usually less than 100 ppm.

The toxic effect of CO on the body is caused primarily by a reaction between CO and the hemoglobin (Hb) of the blood. Hemoglobin normally functions in the blood as a transport system to carry oxygen in the form of oxyhemoglobin (O_2Hb) from the lungs to the body cells and CO_2 from the cells to the lungs (as CO_2Hb). Hemoglobin can also form a compound, carboxyhemoglobin (COHb), with CO. When such a reaction occurs, the ability of the blood to transport oxygen is reduced. The affinity of CO for hemoglobin is more than 200 times greater than that of O_2, and as a result, COHb rather than O_2Hb is formed when both possibilities exist.

The important factor concerning CO effects on the human body is the amount of COHb present in the blood: the higher the percentage of hemoglobin bound up in the form of COHb, the more serious is the effect, as indicated in Table 2-4.

TABLE 2-4 HEALTH EFFECTS OF COHb BLOOD LEVELS

COHb BLOOD LEVEL (%)	DEMONSTRATED EFFECTS
Less than 1.0	No apparent effect.
1.0 to 2.0	Some evidence of effect on behavioral performance.
2.0 to 5.0	Central nervous system effects. Impairment of time-interval discrimination, visual acuity, brightness discrimination and certain other psychomotor functions.
Greater than 5.0	Cardiac and pulmonary functional changes.
10.0 to 80.0	Headache, fatigue, drowsiness, coma, respiratory failure, death.

Redrawn, with permission, from table in *Environmental Science and Technology* 5:213 (1971).

The level of COHb in the blood is directly related to the CO concentration of the inhaled air. For a given ambient air CO concentration, the COHb level in the blood will reach an equilibrium concentration after a sufficient time period. This equilibrium COHb level will be maintained in the blood as long as the ambient air CO level remains unchanged. However, the COHb level will slowly change in the same direction as the CO concentration of the ambient air as a new equilibrium is established.

The normal or background level of blood COHb is about 0.5%. Part of this is the result of CO produced by the body during the destructive metabolism of heme, a component of hemoglobin. The remainder comes from low levels of CO in the ambient air. The equilibrium percentage of COHb in the bloodstream of a person continually exposed to an ambient air CO concentration of less than 100 ppm can easily be estimated by the following equation:

$$\%\text{COHb in blood} = 0.16 \times (\text{CO conc. of air in ppm}) + 0.5 \qquad \text{(eq. 2-5)}$$

The 0.5 is the normal background percentage of COHb in blood. The numbers shown in Table 2-5 were obtained by using this equation.

TABLE 2-5 BLOOD COHb-AIR CO EQUILIBRIUM DATA

AMBIENT AIR CO CONCENTRATION (ppm)	EQUILIBRIUM CONCENTRATION OF BLOOD COHb (%)
10	2.1
20	3.7
30	5.3
50	8.5
70	11.7

The length of time required for the blood COHb level to reach equilibrium with the ambient air CO concentration is a function of the physical activity of the exposed person. Equilibrium is reached more rapidly in people involved in strenuous activity, as illustrated in Fig. 2-4 (notice the two different time scales). Thus, an overlap does exist between the levels of CO in polluted air and the levels which result in observable effects on humans. Man is apparently not as immune to present levels of CO pollution as are plants.

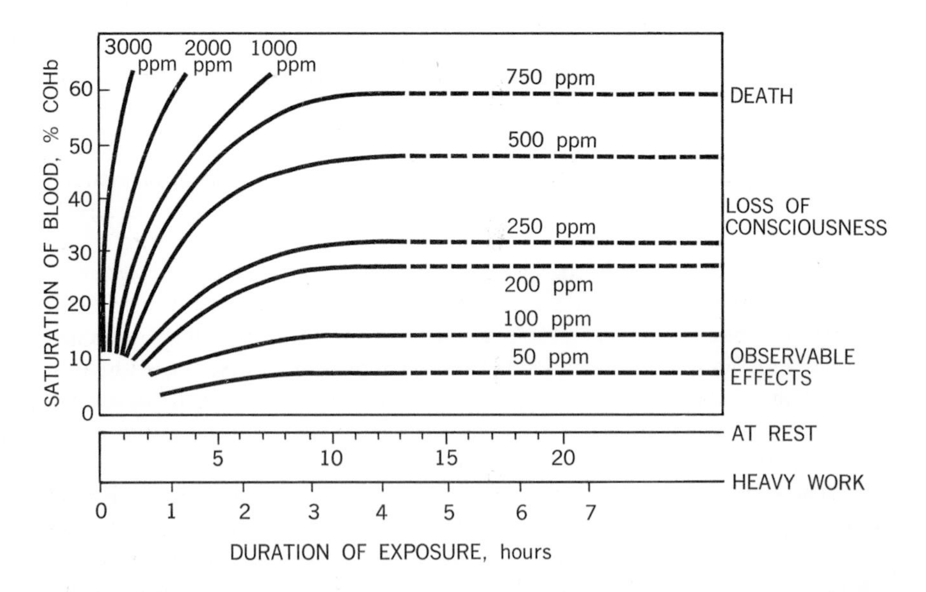

FIGURE 2-4 Acute effects. COHb Levels in the Blood Depend upon the Amount of CO in the Atmosphere, Duration of Exposure, and Type of Physical Activity.

Redrawn, with permission, from *Environmental Science and Technology* 5:213 (1971).

Although it is not considered by many to be pollution, an individualized pollution of the air takes place during smoking. Cigarette smoke contains a CO concentration greater than 20,000 ppm. During inhalation, this is diluted to a level of about 400–500 ppm. This high level of CO in the inhaled air results in a higher COHb level in the blood of smokers as compared to nonsmokers. Table 2-6 contains typical data collected in a study which illustrate this point very well.

TABLE 2-6 BLOOD COHb LEVELS OF SMOKERS

CATEGORY OF SMOKER	MEDIAN EQUILIBRIUM BLOOD LEVEL OF COHb (%)
Never smoked	1.3
Ex-smoker	1.4
Pipe and/or cigar smoker only	1.7
Light cigarette smoker (½ pack or less/day) noninhaler	2.3
Light cigarette smoker (½ pack or less/day) inhaler	3.8
Moderate cigarette smoker (½ to 2 packs/day) inhaler	5.9
Heavy cigarette smoker (2 or more packs/day) inhaler	6.9

Data selected from U.S. Dept. of Health, Education, and Welfare, *Air Quality Criteria for Carbon Monoxide*, p. 9-8.

Control of CO Pollution

A great amount of effort is being expended in attempts to control CO pollution of the air. Most of this effort is directed at the automobile, because 64% of all CO emissions come from transportation sources, and the gasoline-fueled internal combustion engine accounts for most of it. The problem of dealing with the internal combustion engine is complicated, however, for in addition to CO there are also NO_x, HC, and particulate emissions to contend with. (These three other types of pollutant are the topics of the next three chapters.) The important point is that the exhaust of the internal combustion engine is a complex mixture of materials. Control methods applied to one pollutant might affect the amounts of other pollutants produced. This relationship among three of the pollutants present in automobile exhaust is shown in Fig. 2-5.

Notice that a low air-fuel ratio, which minimizes NO_x emissions, results in a high level of CO and HC emissions. The stoichiometric mixture gives low HC and CO values but large amounts of NO_x. The apparent solution, according to Fig. 2-5, is to use high air-fuel ratios. This solution presents difficult engine design problems, and if the air-fuel ratio is raised too much, HC emissions again increase.

The recognition of the internal combustion engine as a major source of pollution has resulted in legislative restrictions which will become increasingly stringent in the future. The trend can be seen in the figures of Table 2-7.

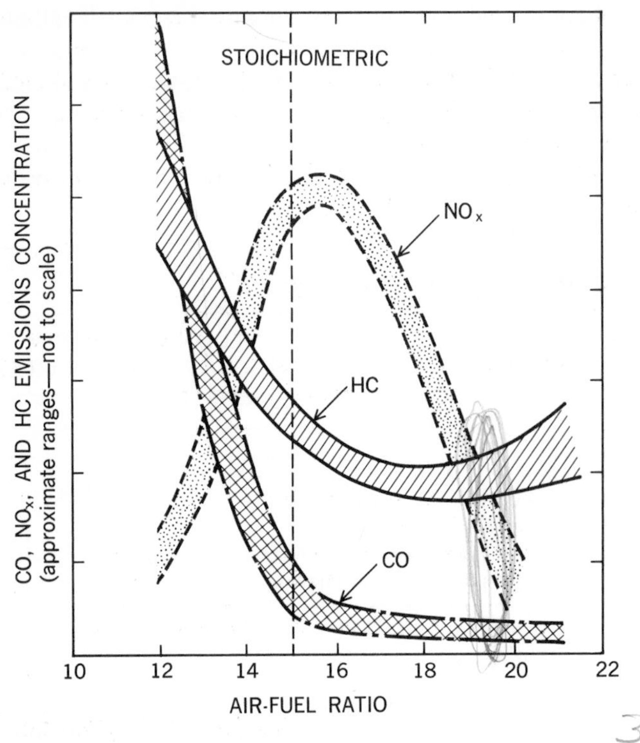

FIGURE 2-5 EFFECTS OF AIR-FUEL RATIO ON EXHAUST COMPOSITION

Redrawn from U.S. Dept. of Health, Education, and Welfare, *Control Techniques for Carbon Monoxide, Nitrogen Oxide, and Hydrocarbon Emission from Mobile Sources*, p. 1-1.

TABLE 2-7 U.S. FEDERAL AUTO EMISSION STANDARDS (GRAMS PER MILE)

	PRIOR TO CONTROL	1970 STANDARDS	PROPOSED STANDARDS 1975	EMISSIONS GOAL FOR 1980
Hydrocarbons	11	2.2	0.5	0.25
Carbon monoxide	80	23	11.0	4.7
Oxides of nitrogen	4	—	0.9	0.4
Particulates	0.3	—	0.1	0.03

Adapted from U.S. Government Printing Office, *Cleaner Air for the Nation* (1970), p. 11.

Four approaches to emission controls for automobiles have been and are still being investigated. These are:

1. Modification of internal combustion engines to reduce the amounts of pollutants formed during fuel combustion.
2. Development of exhaust system reactors which will complete the com-

bustion process and change potential pollutants into more acceptable materials.
3. Development of substitute fuels for gasoline which will produce low concentrations of pollutants upon combustion.
4. Development of low pollution-producing power sources to replace the internal combustion engine.

The first 2 of these possible solutions have been most actively pursued. The principal efforts toward the first solution have involved combustion chamber design changes and carburetor modifications. Improvements in combustion chamber design have reduced the quenching zone in which CO, present in a high-temperature equilibrium with CO_2 and O, is frozen out of the mixture by rapid cooling. Also, better combustion has been produced by designing chambers that cause turbulence in the air-fuel mixture. Carburetor modifications prevent an air-fuel mixture, overly rich in fuel, to be produced. As shown in Fig. 2-5, rich mixtures form large amounts of CO and HC upon combustion.

Most improvements in pre-1971 automobile emission performance were accomplished by engine modifications. It does not appear that further changes of this type, used alone, will enable future emission standards to be met.

In order to meet the standards set for 1975, a great amount of effort is being put into the development of exhaust system reactors. The basic principle used in these reactors is quite simple: in the case of CO emissions, a chemical reaction outside the engine completes the oxidation or burning of CO to CO_2.

Two types of exhaust reactors are being developed. The *thermal exhaust reactor* consists of a high temperature chamber attached to the engine. As hot exhaust passes through the chamber, outside air is added and provides oxygen for the completion of the combustion process. The problem with the thermal reactor has been primarily the lack of an economical material from which the chamber can be built. The material must be able to withstand high temperatures, it must heat up quickly, and it must be resistant to corrosion, especially from lead salts.

The second type of reactor, called a *catalytic reactor*, utilizes a bed of granular catalyst material which becomes activated at moderate temperatures. Exhaust gases are mixed with air and passed over the activated catalyst material. In the presence of the catalyst, oxidation is completed at a much lower temperature than is possible in the thermal reactor. A diagrammatical representation of the two types of exhaust reactors is given in Fig. 2-6. The greatest problem with catalytic reactors is the present lack of a sufficiently durable (50,000 driven miles) catalytic material. The catalysts now in use are subject to poisoning (deactivation) by the adsorption of materials on their surfaces. One of the most effective catalyst poisons is lead, and this provides one reason for the development of lead-free gasoline.

The removal of lead from gasoline is not the simple operation it might seem to be because of a chain effect initiated by the removal. Lead is usually added to gasoline in the form of the compound tetraethyl lead [$Pb(C_2H_5)_4$] as

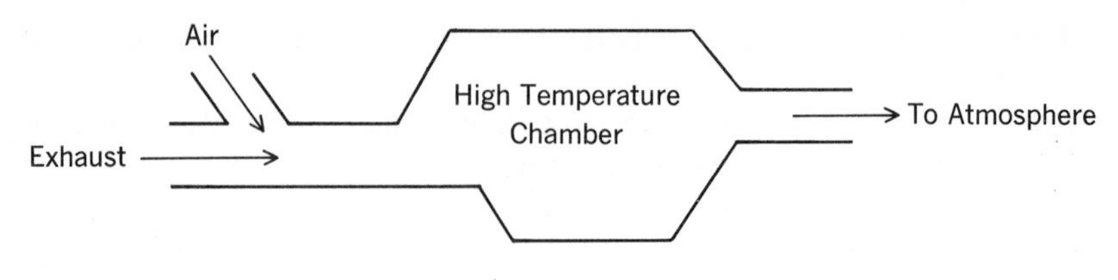

(A) THERMAL EXHAUST REACTOR

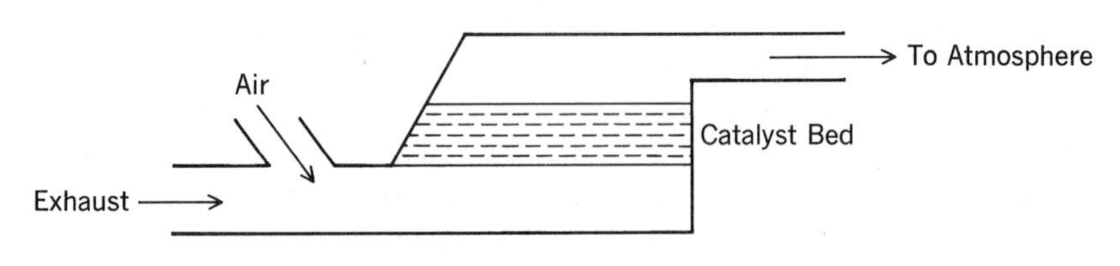

(B) CATALYTIC EXHAUST REACTOR

FIGURE 2-6 EXHAUST REACTORS

a means of increasing the octane rating of the gasoline. The octane rating is a number related to the tendency of a gasoline to cause engine knocking when used as a fuel. The knocking is caused by uneven burning of the fuel inside the engine. Fuels with higher octane ratings have lower tendencies to knock. High compression ratios in engines increase this knocking tendency but also allow more power to be built into smaller engines, and this improves the gas mileage. Despite the increased knocking tendency of such engines, the automotive industry has moved to the use of higher and higher compression ratios in engines, with the result that higher octane fuels are needed.

High octane gasoline can be produced by blending the proper components obtained from refined petroleum. Not enough of the necessary components are obtained from the conventional refining of petroleum, and the needed components can be produced in larger amounts only by further treatment of the refined petroleum. As a result, the cheapest way to increase the octane rating has been found to be the addition of lead compounds.

The pros and cons of removing lead from gasoline indicate the arguments that must be weighed before making such a decision.

The pros are:

1. Catalytic exhaust reactors become more practical.
2. The amount of lead released into the atmosphere is decreased (lead pollution is the topic of Chapter 10).
3. Corrosion of metallic engine and exhaust components is reduced.

The cons are:

1. The octane rating of gasoline is decreased drastically unless expensively

produced petroleum components are added, and the cost of gasoline goes up.

2. New refining equipment would have to be built to produce the necessary additives in quantity, and the cost of gasoline goes up.
3. The needed blending components come from petroleum, therefore a dwindling supply of crude oil will be used still more rapidly. The supply decreases while the demand increases and, again, the cost of gasoline goes up.
4. Lower compression-ratio engines will be developed to use lower octane gasoline. These engines will not be as efficient as the higher-compression models. Economy losses as high as 5%, compared to 1970 model automobiles, have been predicted.

The public, hopefully after weighing such pros and cons, seems generally to favor the removal of anti-knock lead compounds from gasoline. As a result, many models of automobiles manufactured in 1971 and later contain modified engines capable of using lower octane fuels. A limited amount of lead-free gasoline is now on the market (at a higher cost than leaded gasoline).

The total removal of lead compounds from gasoline will probably have to be done over an extended period of time. In the meantime, low-lead gasolines, containing $\frac{1}{2}$ g/gal Pb compared to the present 4 g/gal, will probably appear on the market. This fuel can be made by 20–50% of the petroleum industry with only slight modifications to existing equipment.

The third possible solution to CO pollution problems, a substitute fuel for gasoline, has not proved successful because of shortages and other problems. Natural gas in both compressed (CNG) and liquefied form (LNG) has been used as a fuel. This material, which consists mostly of methane (CH_4), is an attractive, clean-burning fuel, but it is in extremely short supply and presents severe economic problems of containment or storage.

Liquefied petroleum gas (LPG), mainly a mixture of propane (C_3H_8) and butane (C_4H_{10}), is also an attractive fuel. It is more available than natural gas but still presents significant supply problems when considered as a gasoline replacement.

Alcohols have been proposed as gasoline substitutes, but they create problems of their own when combustion products are considered. High concentrations of aldehydes are produced, and these substances are known to contribute to eye irritation and the production of photochemical smog. With the possible exception of fleet car use of LPG, it appears that gasoline will continue to be the only widely used automobile fuel in the immediate future.

The fourth possible solution to the emission-control problem, a substitute for the internal combustion engine, has not been without advocates. Steam, electric, and gas turbine engines are among the alternate power sources being investigated. Although all of these can be developed with lower emission levels than those of comparable internal combustion engines, none of them has been demonstrated to be as simple, economical, flexible, convenient, and acceptable to the public as the present gasoline-fueled internal combustion engine.

The most promising of these substitutes for the near future is the gas turbine. It will be used in some trucks and buses in the immediate future. However, production expenses and unresolved technical problems make its use prohibitive in passenger cars at present.

Suggestions for Further Reading

Journal Articles

1. Bolin, B. 1970. The carbon cycle. *Scientific American* 223:125–32.
2. Inman, R. E., et al. 1971. Soil: a natural sink for carbon monoxide. *Science* 172:1229–30.
3. Wolf, P. C. 1971. Carbon monoxide—measurement and monitoring in urban air. *Environmental Science and Technology* 5:212–18.

Government Documents

1. U.S. Dept. of Commerce. 1971. *Automotive fuels and air pollution.*
2. U.S. Dept. of Commerce 1971. *Exhaust emissions from gas turbine and aircraft engines.* Sub-council report, National Industrial Pollution Control Council.
3. U.S. Dept. of Health, Education, and Welfare. 1970. *Air quality criteria for carbon monoxide.* National Air Pollution Control Administration Publication No. AP-62.
4. U.S. Dept. of Health, Education, and Welfare. 1970. *Control techniques for carbon monoxide emissions, from stationary sources.* National Air Pollution Control Administration Publication No. AP-65.
5. U.S. Dept. of Health, Education, and Welfare. 1970. *Control techniques for carbon monoxide, nitrogen oxide, and hydrocarbon emissions from mobile sources.* National Air Pollution Control Administration Publication No. AP-66.

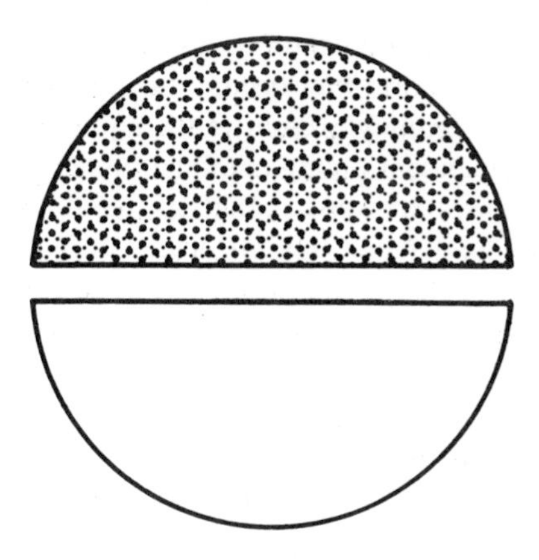

Chapter 3

Oxides of Nitrogen

Basic Chemical Reactions

The term NO_x will be used in this chapter to represent the composite atmospheric concentrations of the gases nitric oxide (NO) and nitrogen dioxide (NO_2). Although other nitrogen oxides exist, these two, under urban atmospheric conditions, are the ones primarily involved in air pollution. Nitric oxide is a colorless, odorless gas. In contrast, nitrogen dioxide has a reddish-brown color and a pungent, choking odor.

The lower oxide, NO, is emitted into the atmosphere in much larger quantities than NO_2. This is the opposite of the situation with carbon oxides discussed in the previous chapter, where the higher of the two oxides (CO_2) is emitted in the largest amount.

The basic chemistry of formation of NO and NO_2 involves the reaction of nitrogen and oxygen of the air to give NO and then further reaction of NO with more oxygen to give NO_2. The equations representing these reactions are:

$$N_2 + O_2 \rightleftharpoons 2NO \qquad \text{(eq. 3-1)}$$

$$2NO + O_2 \rightleftharpoons 2NO_2 \qquad \text{(eq. 3-2)}$$

Air is composed approximately of 80% nitrogen and 20% oxygen by volume. At room temperature these two gases have very little tendency to react with each other. At higher temperatures (above 1210°C or 2000°F) they react, by equation 3-1, to give significant amounts (in terms of pollutant concentrations) of nitric oxide. Since temperatures in the 1210°C–1765°C (2000°F–3000°F) range are commonly reached during many combustion processes involving air, this reaction is important as a source of NO. The reaction may be thought of as a side reaction that occurs during combustion.

The amount of NO actually present in the equilibrium mixture resulting from this reaction is dependent on the combustion temperature, the length of time the combustion gases are kept at that temperature, and the amount of excess oxygen present in the flame. The effects of combustion temperature and residence time of gases at that temperature can be seen from Table 3-1. Equilibrium NO concentrations are given at several temperatures, together with the time required for 500 ppm of NO to form at that temperature. These data are for a gas mixture containing 75% N_2 and 3% O_2. This mixture approximates reaction conditions in combustion processes since the majority of the oxygen present in air reacts with the substance undergoing combustion.

TABLE 3-1 TEMPERATURE DEPENDENCE OF NO FORMATION

TEMPERATURE	NO CONC. AT EQUILIBRIUM (ppm)	TIME TO FORM 500 ppm NO (sec)
27°C (80°F)	1.1×10^{-10}	—
527°C (980°F)	0.77	—
1316°C (2400°F)	550	1370
1538°C (2800°F)	1380	162
1760°C (3200°F)	2600	1.10
1980°C (3600°F)	4150	0.117

Data compiled from U.S. Dept. of Health, Education, and Welfare, *Control Techniques for Nitrogen Oxide Emissions from Stationary Sources*, p. 3-1 and p. 4-2.

The dependence of this reaction on oxygen concentrations can be seen by a comparison of the equilibrium concentrations given in Table 3-1 with those that result from the same reaction carried out in air (80% N_2 and 20% O_2). Such a comparison shows that the equilibrium concentrations in air are approximately three times those in the 75% N_2:3% O_2 mixture.

Because NO formation is favored only at high temperatures, the NO in a high-temperature equilibrium mixture will dissociate back to N_2 and O_2 if the temperature of the mixture is lowered slowly enough to allow sufficient time. If, on the other hand, an equilibrium mixture is cooled suddenly, much of the NO persists in the low-temperature mixture. Such rapid cooling of products is characteristic of combustion processes.

The formation of NO_2 from NO and O_2 involves equation 3-2. This reaction does not account for much NO_2, even in excess air. This contrasts with the rapid reaction of CO to form CO_2 in excess air. The reasons for the lack of rapid NO_2 formation are related to the particular temperature and concentration dependence of the rate or speed of the reaction. This reaction is one of just a few that slows down as the temperature increases. Therefore, at high temperatures little NO_2 is formed rapidly enough to appear in exhaust gases.

At a temperature of 1100°C (2000°F), the amount of NO_2 formed is usually less than 0.5% of the total NO_x. At lower temperatures, where the rate would be expected to be greater, concentration-dependence factors affect the rate in a negative way.

The reaction rate is dependent on the oxygen concentration and on the square of the NO concentration. A doubling of the NO concentration causes the reaction to go four times as fast, and a halving of the NO concentration causes the rate to become one-fourth as great. As NO is ejected into the air along with other exhaust gases, it is rapidly cooled (in a matter of seconds) and diluted by a factor of about 100. The reaction rate would drop to $\frac{1}{10{,}000}$ $\left[\frac{1}{(100)^2}\right]$ of its previous (undiluted) value because of the drop in NO concentration. The increased amount of oxygen and the lower temperature cause a slight increase in the rate: the net effect is that only about 10% of the NO produced in the combustion process is converted to NO_2 during the cooling and dilution processes.

Some NO, once it is in the atmosphere, is converted to NO_2 by another process which does not involve a direct reaction with O_2. This process, known as the NO_2 photolytic cycle, is discussed later in this chapter.

Sources of NO_x Pollution

On a global basis, the major proportion of NO_x released into the atmosphere is in the form of NO produced by natural bacterial action. About 50×10^7 tons is produced this way each year. Only about 5×10^7 tons per year of NO_x come from man-made sources. The problem of NO_x pollution from man is not so much one of amount as it is of distribution: natural sources distribute the NO_x evenly over the globe, while man-made sources cause high concentrations in limited areas.

The NO_x concentration in urban atmospheres is 10–100 times greater than in nonurban atmospheres. Typically the concentration of NO_x on the North American continent which can be attributed to natural sources is about 2 ppb (parts per *billion*) NO and 4 ppb NO_2. In urban atmospheres concentrations as high as 0.5 ppm (500 ppb) may be reached. The nitrogen oxide emissions (like those of CO) are closely related to population densities, because the major man-made source is combustion; and most combustion is related to the automobile, power production, or waste disposal. Numerical data in support of this statement are given in Table 3-2.

Notice that 18 million tons/year or 88% of the estimated yearly emissions come from the combustion of coal, oil, natural gas, or gasoline. Of the 10 million tons produced annually in stationary combustion sources, power plants account for 4 million, industries for 4.8 million, and home and commercial heating plants the remaining 1.2 million tons per year. Relatively small quantities are produced by noncombustion industrial sources such as nitric

TABLE 3-2 NATIONWIDE NITROGEN OXIDES EMISSIONS, 1968

SOURCE	EMISSIONS, 10^6 TONS/YR			PERCENTAGE OF TOTAL		
Transportation	8.1			39.3		
Motor vehicles		7.2			34.9	
Gasoline			6.6			32.0
Diesel			0.6			2.9
Aircraft		N[a]			N	
Railroads		0.4			1.9	
Vessels		0.2			1.0	
Nonhighway use of motor fuels		0.3			1.5	
Fuel combustion in stationary sources	10.0			48.5		
Coal		4.0			19.4	
Fuel oil		1.0			4.8	
Natural gas[b]		4.8			23.3	
Wood		0.2		1.0		
Industrial processes	0.2			1.0		
Solid waste disposal	0.6			2.9		
Miscellaneous	1.7			8.3		
Forest fires		1.2			5.8	
Structural fires		N			N	
Coal refuse burning		0.2			1.0	
Agricultural burning		0.3			1.5	
Total	20.6			100.0		

[a]N = Negligible.
[b]Includes LPG and kerosene.

Adapted from U.S. Dept. of Health, Education, and Welfare, *Nationwide Inventory of Air Pollutant Emissions—1968*, p. 15.

acid plants. However, the environmental impact of even these small amounts can be large because of localized concentrations.

The Photolytic Cycle of NO_2

Many of the serious effects of NO_x pollution result, not from the oxides themselves, but from their role in the formation of photochemical oxidants which are the more harmful components of smog. This oxidant production results when other pollutants upset a group of naturally occurring atmospheric reactions involving NO and NO_2. These reactions, collectively known as the NO_2 photolytic cycle, are a direct consequence of an interaction between sunlight and NO_2. The steps in this cycle, illustrated in Fig. 3-1, are:

1. NO_2 absorbs energy in the form of ultraviolet light from the sun.
2. The absorbed energy breaks the NO_2 molecules into NO molecules and oxygen atoms (O). The atomic oxygen produced is very reactive.
3. Atomic oxygen atoms react with atmospheric oxygen (O_2) to produce ozone (O_3), a secondary pollutant.
4. The ozone reacts with NO to give NO_2 and O_2, and the cycle is complete.

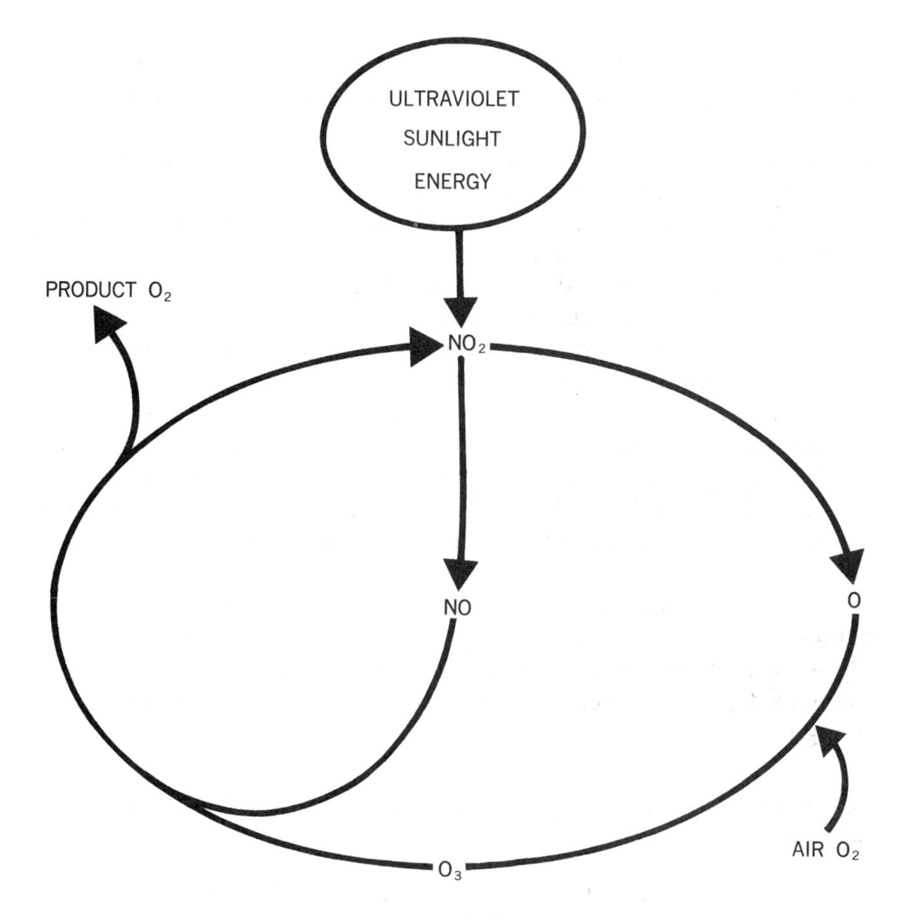

FIGURE 3-1 PHOTOLYTIC NO_2 CYCLE

Redrawn from U.S. Dept. of Health, Education, and Welfare, *Air Quality Criteria for Nitrogen Oxides*, p. 2-3.

The net effect of this cycle is the rapid cycling of NO_2, and if it were not for competing reactants in the atmosphere, the cycle would produce no overall net effect. The ambient NO and NO_2 concentrations would not change since O_3 and NO would be formed and destroyed in equal quantities.

The competing reactions involve hydrocarbons which are often emitted from the same sources as NO_x. The hydrocarbons interact in such a way that the cycle is unbalanced and NO is converted into NO_2 faster than NO_2 is dissociated into NO and O. This effect also results in a buildup of ozone in the atmosphere. This unbalancing of the NO_2 cycle will be discussed in more detail in Chapter 4.

Concentration and Distribution of NO_x

During a typical day in a city, ambient NO_x levels follow a regular pattern related to sunlight and traffic. The pattern, illustrated in Fig. 3-2, is:

1. Before daylight, NO and NO_2 levels remain fairly stable at a concentration slightly higher than the daily minimum.
2. As human activity increases (6–8 A.M.), the level of NO goes up mainly because of automobile traffic.
3. As the sun comes up and provides ultraviolet light, the NO_2 level goes up because of the conversion of primary NO into secondary NO_2.
4. Ozone begins to accumulate as the NO concentration diminishes to a level of less than 0.1 ppm.
5. As solar intensity decreases and automobile traffic increases in the evening (5–8 P.M.), the concentration of NO again goes up.
6. Solar energy is unavailable to convert NO to NO_2 (through hydrocarbon interaction) but O_3, built up during the day, does react with NO. The result is an increase in NO_2 and a decrease in O_3 levels.

Continuous measurements have shown that peak values of NO concentration between 1–2 ppm are common, but that NO_2 concentrations are usually about 0.5 ppm. Table 3-3 gives the maximum concentrations of NO and NO_2 recorded in various cities between 1962 and 1968. The values are 1-hour averages.

TABLE 3-3 MAXIMUM NO_x LEVELS, 1962–1968

CITY	MAXIMUM NO CONCENTRATION (ppm)	MAXIMUM NO_2 CONCENTRATION (ppm)
Chicago	0.91	0.47
Cincinnati	1.38	0.56
Denver	0.54	0.33
Los Angeles	1.42	0.68
Philadelphia	1.87	0.32
St. Louis	0.75	0.22
San Francisco	1.30	0.41
Washington, D.C.	1.14	0.30

Data selected from U.S. Dept. of Health, Education, and Welfare, *Air Quality Criteria for Nitrogen Oxides*, pp. 6-10–6-13.

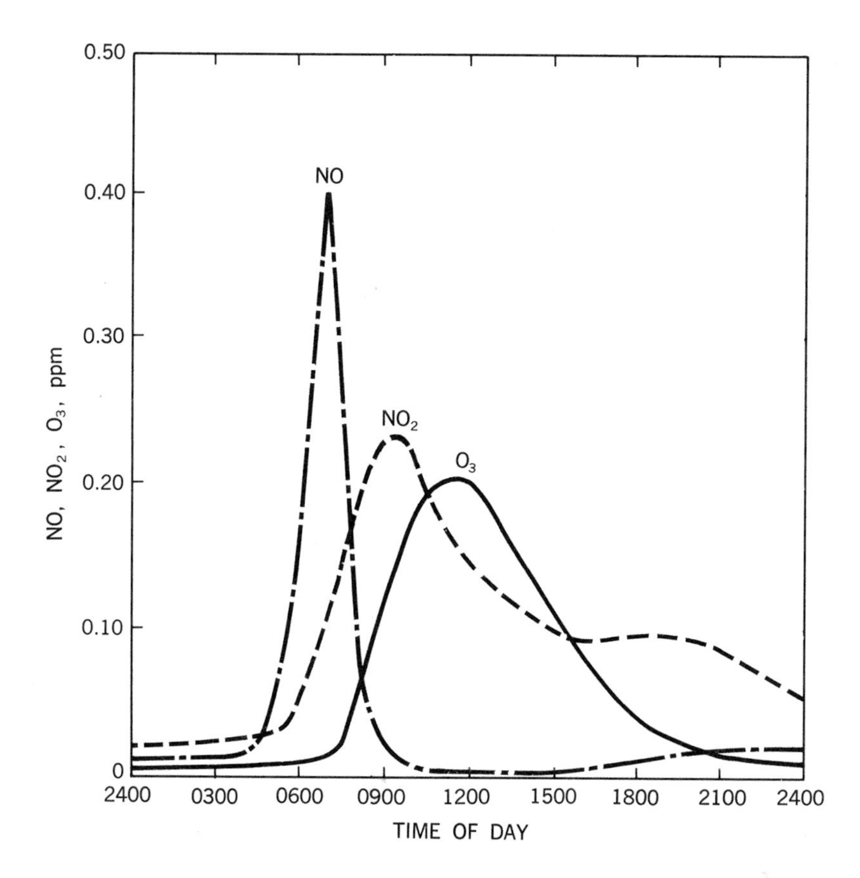

FIGURE 3-2 Average Daily 1-Hour Concentrations of Selected Pollutants in Los Angeles, California, July 19, 1965.

Redrawn, with modifications, from U.S. Dept. of Health, Education and Welfare, *Air Quality Criteria for Nitrogen Oxides*, p. 6-2.

The Fate of Atmospheric NO_x

On the basis of estimated global background levels and annual emission rates for NO_x, the average residence time of NO_2 in the atmosphere is estimated to be about 3 days, and that of NO about 4 days. These residence times indicate that natural processes, including photochemical reactions, result in the removal of these oxides. The ultimate end product of NO_x pollution is nitric acid, which is subsequently precipitated as nitrate salts in either rainfall or as dust.

The mechanism for atmospheric formation of nitric acid from NO_2 has not been completely determined. It is known that the direct reaction of NO_2 with H_2O according to the equations

$$2NO_2 + H_2O \rightarrow HNO_3 + HNO_2 \qquad \text{(eq. 3-3)}$$

or

$$3NO_2 + H_2O \rightarrow 2HNO_3 + NO \qquad \text{(eq. 3-4)}$$

is of little importance. Calculations using the normally encountered NO, NO_2, and H_2O concentrations of urban atmospheres show an equilibrium concentration of about 1.0 ppb HNO_3 for the second reaction, and a rate of 0.1 ppb per hour, which appears to be too slow to account for the observed residence times given above.

A possible mechanism for the formation of HNO_3 in polluted air has been proposed. At the maximum NO_2 concentration, ozone becomes important and the following series of reactions might take place:

$$O_3 + NO_2 \rightarrow NO_3 + O_2 \qquad \text{(eq. 3-5)}$$

$$NO_3 + NO_2 \rightarrow N_2O_5 \qquad \text{(eq. 3-6)}$$

$$N_2O_5 + H_2O \rightarrow 2HNO_3 \qquad \text{(eq. 3-7)}$$

This mechanism is still conjectural, and much work remains to be done to determine the exact route followed. However, the important thing to remember is that atmospheric processes eventually cause NO_x to be changed into HNO_3, which rapidly reacts to form various particulate nitrates.

Effects of NO_x on Plants

The presence of NO_x in the atmosphere does lead to plant injury and damage. It is difficult to determine just which of the effects result directly from NO_x and which result from secondary pollutants produced in the photolytic cycle of NO_2. A number of the secondary pollutants have definitely been shown to be very damaging to plants. These substances and the damage they cause are discussed in Chapter 4.

Evidence of damage to plants resulting from direct exposure to atmospheric NO_x is usually limited to observations made in the proximity of specific industrial sources or those made in the laboratory. Damage to plants from high atmospheric levels of NO_2 has been observed near nitric acid production facilities. No evidence of NO damage to plants has been observed outside the laboratory.

Controlled laboratory experiments have provided most of what is known concerning NO_x plant toxicities. Cotton, pinto bean, and endive plants were fumigated with NO_2 (1.0 ppm) for 48 hours. All showed slight but definite spotting of the leaves. After a 21-hour exposure to 3.5 ppm, spots of mild necrosis (rotting or tissue breakdown) were observed on the leaves of cotton and bean plants, while the endive was completely necrotic.

Fumigation of bean and tomato plants with 10 ppm NO resulted in an immediate 60 to 70% decrease in the rate of photosynthesis as measured by CO_2 absorption. The CO_2 absorption rate returned to normal as soon as the

NO fumigations were discontinued. No visible plant injury developed after exposure.

The effects of exposure to low levels of NO_2 for extended time periods are less evident, and it is this type of effect that would more closely approximate those occurring in polluted air. Extended exposure of pinto bean plants to 0.3 ppm NO_2 and tomato plants to a concentration range of 0.15 to 0.26 ppm NO_2 both resulted in very mild changes in the pigmented patterns of leaf tissue. An 8-month exposure to 0.25 ppm NO_2 resulted in increased leaf drop and reduced yield for navel orange trees. The study of low level concentrations (less than 1 ppm) of NO_x on plants is an area in which much research remains to be done.

Effects of NO_x on Humans

Both oxides of nitrogen under discussion, NO and NO_2, are potential health hazards. Animal mortality studies indicate that NO_2 is about four times more toxic than NO. No cases of human death from NO poisoning have been reported. At the concentrations found in the atmosphere, NO is not an irritant and is not considered a health hazard. The greatest toxic potential it has, at ambient air concentrations, is its ability to undergo oxidation and become the more toxic NO_2.

In test animals exposed to very high concentrations of NO, central nervous system paralysis and convulsions have been observed. In one study, mice were exposed to a level of 2500 ppm NO. After a 6–7 minute exposure, the mice were narcotized but recovered after a 4–6 minute exposure to fresh air. However, the effects of a 12-minute exposure were not reversible, and all the mice died.

The more toxic NO_2 exerts its main toxic effect on the lungs. Most available information comes from studies conducted on animals in the laboratory. Concentrations of NO_2 greater than 100 ppm are lethal to most animal species, and 90% of the resulting deaths are caused by pulmonary edema. Table 3-4 contains data related to such studies. The animals used included cats, guinea pigs, mice, rats, and rabbits.

TABLE 3-4 TOXIC EFFECTS OF NO_2 ON ANIMALS

CONCENTRATION OF NO_2 (ppm)	TIME TILL DEATH (MINUTES)	PERCENTAGE OF DEATHS
30	—	0
100	318	74
150	90	70
400	58	92
600	32	93
800	29	100
1000	19	100

Adapted from U.S. Dept. of Health, Education, and Welfare, *Air Quality Criteria for Nitrogen Oxides*, p. 9-3.

The small amount of information available concerning toxicological effects of NO_2 in man is for levels higher than those found in ambient air. Experimental exposure of volunteer subjects to 5 ppm NO_2 for 10 minutes produced a substantial but transient increase in the resistance of the lung airways to air movement.

Numerous possibilities exist for occupational exposure to NO_x. Especially hazardous occupational operations are: the manufacturing of NO, the nitration of cellulose and other materials, electric-arc welding, and photoengraving. Accidental exposures to high NO_x levels have resulted from the combustion of celluloid and nitrocellulose film and the inhalation of silage gas.

Effects of NO_x on Materials

Field studies and laboratory investigations have successfully linked nitrogen oxides (NO_x) and their reaction products (nitrates) to problems related to textile dyes, textile fibers, and nickel-brass alloys. Some textile dyes will fade upon exposure to NO_x. The dyes include those used on acetate rayon, cotton, and viscose rayon. The cotton fading problem came to light in the mid-1950s, when housewives complained of cotton fabrics fading when dried in home gas-fired dryers. The fading was traced to oxides of nitrogen formed during the combustion of natural gas used to heat the dryers. The NO_x level in such dryers was found to be between 0.6 and 2.0 ppm.

Information concerning the damaging effects of NO_x on textile fibers is meager. A study of cotton fibers exposed to air containing above average levels of NO_x found up to 10% loss of fiber strength in the tested materials. In March, 1964, New York newspapers reported an episode of excessive runs in nylon stockings worn by women in the vicinity of a demolition project. The problem was traced to abnormal levels of ambient air NO_2 levels produced during dynamite blasting operations. A combination of unfavorable weather and NO_2 produced acid aerosols which damaged the nylon.

High levels of particulate nitrates have caused stress-corrosion failures of nickel-brass wire springs in relays used by telephone companies. It was found that high nitrate concentrations in airborne dust, which had accumulated adjacent to cracked areas, produced the failures.

Control of NO_x Pollution

The control of NO_x emissions is an area in which final answers are not all in sight. Attempts to use laboratory results have been plagued by difficulties, and many of the problems relate either directly or indirectly to the fact that most NO_x emissions come from combustion processes in which many variables are involved.

The variables in combustion processes of particular importance in NO_x

control are: (1) many different types of fuel are used; (2) a variety of different combustion devices is used; (3) different flame temperatures are reached; and (4) various other pollutants are present in the combustion products. Because of interplay among these variables, it does not appear likely that one simple technique for general NO_x control is possible. For example, a technique now under development looks promising for application to the control of NO_x from oil-fueled boilers: the same technique shows serious shortcomings when used on coal-fueled boilers. Another technique, used to remove NO_x from exhaust gases, works reasonably well if SO_2 is also present but does not work in its absence. Burning coal produces SO_2, but burning gasoline does not.

Much of the research and development in NO_x control have been directed toward two methods of control. One method involves the modification of combustion conditions as a means of decreasing the amount of NO_x generated. The other method utilizes various devices to remove NO_x from exhaust gases. Much research in these areas is in progress, and much of the following information involves techniques that are still being developed.

Earlier in this chapter it was pointed out that the main factors affecting NO_x production in the form of NO (eq. 3-1) were the flame temperature, the amount of excess air present, and the residence time of reactants at the flame temperature. Higher flame temperatures produce more NO_x. Lower amounts of excess air generally produce smaller amounts of NO_x, but excess air beyond certain levels dilutes the combusting gases, produces a lower flame temperature, and decreases the amount of NO_x. Research has been done on the effect of lower flame temperatures and smaller amounts of excess air on NO_x emissions. Some methods utilizing these approaches are two-stage combustion, exhaust gas recirculation, and steam or water injection. In the two-stage combustion method, the fuel is partially burned with less than stoichiometric amounts of air present. This limits NO production by making excess oxygen unavailable. In the second stage, the fuel combustion is completed after injecting air into the mixture. The removal of heat between stages reduces the temperature at which combustion in excess air takes place and again decreases the amount of NO formed. This method has proved successful for gas-fueled power plants.

The recirculation of exhaust or flue gases back into the combustion chamber lowers the peak flame temperature and lowers the concentration of available oxygen. Both of these effects result in lower NO_x emissions. Laboratory studies show this method to be very effective in reducing NO_x emissions from internal combustion engines.

Steam or water, injected into the combustion chamber, effectively lower the flame temperature. This effect is similar to that obtained by recirculating exhaust gases. Water injection may be preferred over steam because of availability, lower cost, and cooling effectiveness.

The removal of NO_x from exhaust gases has been approached mainly from the points of view of catalytic reactors or absorption systems. The catalytic reduction of NO_x back to elemental N_2 is an area of intensive research, particularly as a solution to the problem of NO_x emissions from automobiles. At present, catalyst durability is a major problem. Available catalysts would require replacement every 8,000 to 15,000 miles with unleaded fuel. This is more often than the desirable 50,000 mile interval. The available catalysts also present problems related to exhaust temperatures and existing fuel lead concentrations.

The development of suitable catalysts would make a dual catalytic system feasible for control of CO, hydrocarbon, and NO_x emissions from automobile exhaust. In such a system, an oxidizing catalyst would convert CO and hydrocarbons to CO_2 and water, while a reducing catalyst would convert NO_x to N_2.

Adsorption methods do not appear feasible for automobile NO_x control, but they might be effective with flue gases. Flue gases are passed over solid or liquid adsorbers which effectively retain the NO_x. Water-based adsorbing systems have proved to be the most effective, especially when the water contains alkaline substances or sulfuric acid. Systems now under development remove NO_2 and sulfur oxides simultaneously, but problems are encountered when the NO_2 occurs without any sulfur oxides.

Suggestions for Further Reading

Journal Articles

1. Delwiche, C. C. 1970. The nitrogen cycle. *Scientific American* 223:137–46.
2. Schuck, E. A., and Stephens, E. R. 1969. Oxides of nitrogen. In *Advances in environmental sciences,* vol. 1, ed. Pitts, J. N., and Metcalf, R. L., pp. 73–118. New York: Wiley-Interscience.

Government Documents

1. Environmental Protection Agency. 1971. *Air quality criteria for nitrogen oxides.* Air Pollution Control Office Publication No. AP-84.
2. U.S. Dept. of Health, Education, and Welfare. 1970. *Control techniques for carbon monoxide, nitrogen oxide, and hydrocarbon emissions from mobile sources.* National Air Pollution Control Administration Publication No. AP-66.
3. U.S. Dept. of Health, Education, and Welfare. 1970. *Control techniques for nitrogen oxides from stationary sources.* National Air Pollution Control Administration Publication No. AP-67.

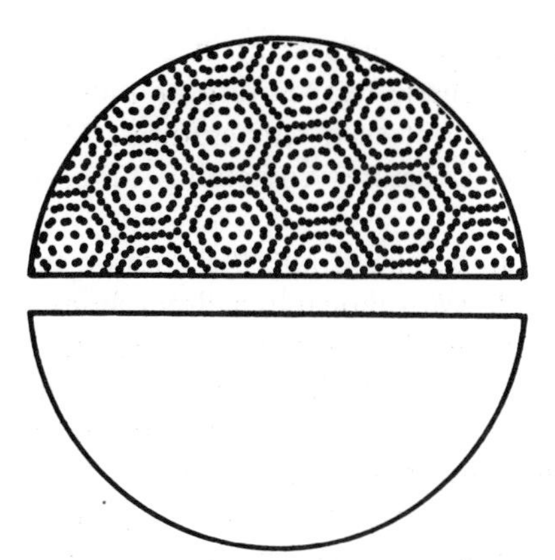

Chapter 4

Hydrocarbons and Photochemical Oxidants

Basic Compounds Involved

Hydrocarbons and photochemical oxidants are two separate, but related, categories of pollutant compounds. Hydrocarbons are primary pollutants, because they are introduced directly into the air. Photochemical oxidants are secondary pollutants originating in the atmosphere from reactions involving primary pollutants. Both groups will be discussed together because the majority of photochemical oxidants originate from reactions in which hydrocarbons are directly or indirectly involved. Any estimate of the effects of atmospheric hydrocarbon pollution must include the contributions made by photochemical oxidants. In fact, most of the principal effects of hydrocarbon pollution are thought to be caused by compounds resulting from atmospheric reactions of hydrocarbons.

Hydrocarbons

These compounds, as their name implies, contain only the elements hydrogen and carbon. Literally tens of thousands of such compounds are known to exist. They are found in all three physical states (gas, liquid, and solid) at room temperatures. The physical state characteristic of each is related to the molecular structure and particularly to the number of carbon atoms making up the molecule. Those containing 1–4 carbon atoms are gases at ordinary temperatures, while those with 5 or more are liquids or solids. In general, the tendency to exist in the solid state increases with an increasing number of carbon atoms.

The hydrocarbons most important in air pollution are those that are gases at normal atmospheric temperature or those that are highly volatile (easily changed to gases) at such temperatures. Most of these compounds have relatively simple structures containing 12 or less carbon atoms per molecule.

Hydrocarbons can be placed into 3 classes on the basis of their general molecular structure. *Acyclic* (aliphatic) hydrocarbons are those containing no rings of carbon atoms in the molecule: all carbon atoms are arranged in chains, with or without branching. *Aromatic* hydrocarbons contain six-membered carbon rings (benezene rings) in their molecules: each carbon atom of the rings has only one additional atom (C or H) attached to it. *Alicyclic* hydrocarbons are those containing a ring structure other than benzene. Examples of these hydrocarbon types are given in Table 4-1.

TABLE 4-1 EXAMPLES OF HYDROCARBON CLASSIFICATION

CLASSIFICATION		
Acyclic	Aromatic	Alicyclic
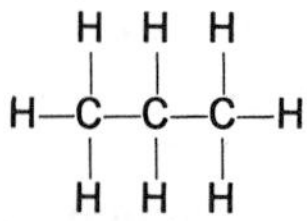 Propane	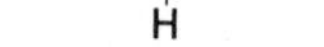 Benzene	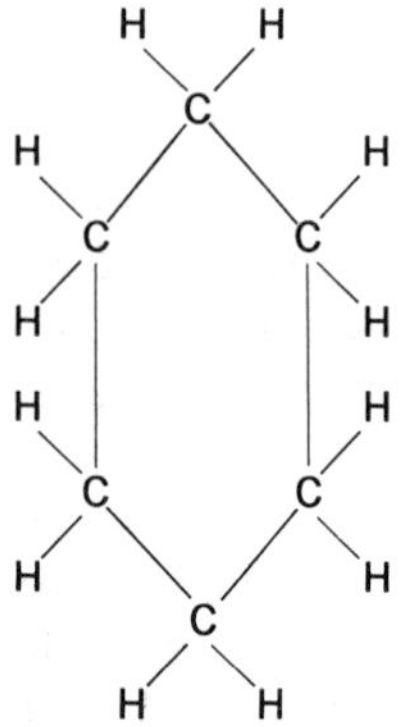 Cyclohexane
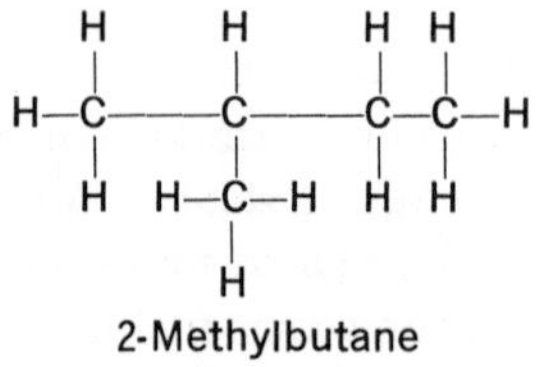 2-Methylbutane	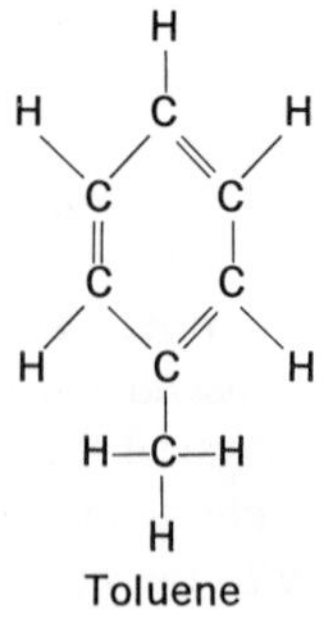 Toluene	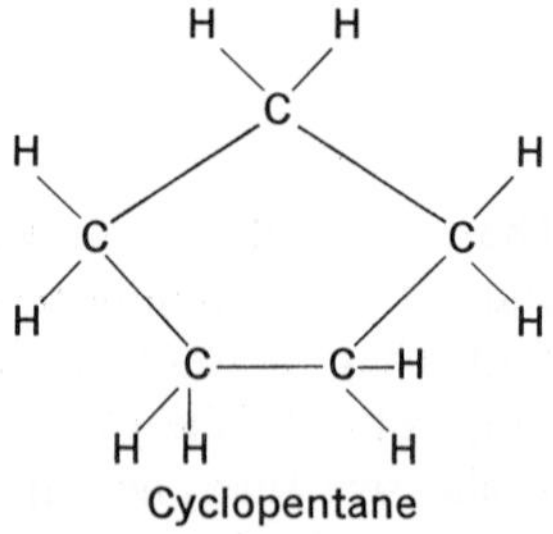 Cyclopentane

The importance of these various classes of compounds will become apparent when their reactivities and toxicities are considered. Both of these properties vary with the compound class.

The number of hydrocarbons involved in air pollution is fairly large. An analysis of urban air by gas chromatography has resulted in the identification of 56 different hydrocarbon compounds. The number present is probably larger, but the sensitivity of the analytical method prevented others, in very low concentrations, from being detected.

In 1965 a series of 200 samples of air was taken in the Los Angeles area, and each sample was analyzed for hydrocarbons. The average concentration of the most abundant ones found are given in Table 4-2.

TABLE 4-2 HYDROCARBONS IN LOS ANGELES AIR, 1965

HYDROCARBON NAME	HYDROCARBON FORMULA	HYDROCARBON CONCENTRATION (ppm)
Methane	CH_4	3.22
Toluene	C_7H_8	0.05
n-Butane	C_4H_{10}	0.06
i-Pentane	C_5H_{12}	0.04
Ethane	C_2H_6	0.10
Benzene	C_6H_6	0.03
n-Pentane	C_5H_{12}	0.03
Propane	C_3H_8	0.05
Ethylene	C_2H_4	0.06

Data selected from U.S. Dept. of Health, Education, and Welfare, *Air Quality Criteria for Hydrocarbons*, p. 3-8.

Photochemical Oxidants

The term *photochemical oxidant* is used to describe an atmospheric substance, produced by a photochemical process (a chemical process that requires light), which will oxidize materials not readily oxidized by gaseous oxygen. These substances are secondary pollutants produced by an interaction of primary pollutants with light.

Hydrocarbons are very much involved in the production of photochemical oxidants. The large variety of hydrocarbons involved in these reactions prevents a simple explanation from being formulated for the various processes. Although the intimate details of the reactions are not known, several specific facts are known quite well. The involvement of the NO_2 photolytic cycle (discussed in Chapter 3) has been definitely established. Two of the most harmful secondary pollutants produced as a result of the involvement of hydrocarbons in this cycle have been identified. These are ozone (O_3), a form of oxygen, and peroxyacetylnitrate $\left(CH_3{-}C{\overset{\displaystyle O}{\underset{\displaystyle OONO_2}{\lessgtr}}} \right)$, the simplest member of a group of compounds, peroxyacylnitrates, usually referred to collectively as PAN.

Ozone is obviously not a hydrocarbon, but its concentration increase in the atmosphere is a direct result of hydrocarbon reactions. PAN is seen to be a hydrocarbon derivative. The mechanisms by which these compounds are produced will be discussed later. Although other photochemical oxidants are produced, we shall limit our discussion to these two because more is known about them, and the others are produced in much smaller quantities. Also, these two are similar to the others and may serve as prototypes for behavior studies.

Sources of Hydrocarbon Pollution

The presence of hydrocarbons (especially methane, CH_4) in the atmosphere from natural sources has been established. Most of these have been traced to biological processes, although small amounts of some are attributed to geothermal activity and processes taking place in coal fields, natural gas and petroleum fields, and naturally occurring fires. The greatest quantity is produced during the decomposition of organic matter on the earth's surface. The background hydrocarbon concentrations for nonurban air have been estimated as 1.0–1.5 ppm of methane, and less than 0.1 ppm for each of the other compounds. The technological or man-made sources of hydrocarbon emission are categorized in Table 4-3.

Notice that again, as with CO and NO_x pollutants, transportation is the main source, contributing slightly more than 50% of the total. Once again, gasoline-fueled vehicles are the main contributor to pollution from transportation sources.

Gasoline, a complex mixture of simple hydrocarbons plus slight amounts of nonhydrocarbon additives, is very volatile and readily evaporates and escapes into the air. Such evaporation, plus the emission of unburned fuel in the exhaust, are the two mechanisms by which automobiles release hydrocarbons into the air. For an automobile equipped with no emission control system, it is estimated that 60% of the emitted hydrocarbons come from the exhaust, 20% escapes from the crankcase, 10% results from evaporation at the carburetor, and 10% evaporates from the fuel tank. Hundreds of different hydrocarbons are emitted in this way into the air, most in trace amounts.

Industrial processes comprise the next largest source. Hydrocarbons are lost to the atmosphere during production, processing, storage, and transfer of products containing them.

Gasoline hydrocarbons are lost in vapor form during the loading of tank trucks, the filling of service station storage tanks, and the filling of automobile fuel tanks.

The evaporation of organic solvents, most of which contain hydrocarbons, accounts for nearly 10% of all industrial emissions. These solvents are important ingredients of paints, varnishes, lacquers, undercoatings, and other

TABLE 4-3 NATIONWIDE HYDROCARBON EMISSIONS, 1968

SOURCE	EMISSIONS, 10^6 TONS/YR			PERCENTAGE OF TOTAL		
Transportation	16.6			51.9		
Motor vehicles		15.6			48.8	
Gasoline			15.2			47.5
Diesel			0.4			1.3
Aircraft		0.3			0.9	
Railroads		0.3			0.9	
Vessels		0.1			0.3	
Non-highway use of motor fuels		0.3			1.0	
Fuel combustion in stationary sources	0.7			2.2		
Coal		0.2			0.6	
Fuel oil		0.1			0.3	
Natural gas		N[a]			N	
Wood		0.4			1.3	
Industrial processes	4.6			14.4		
Solid waste disposal	1.6			5.0		
Miscellaneous	8.5			26.5		
Forest fires		2.2			6.9	
Structural fires		0.1			0.3	
Coal refuse burning		0.2			0.6	
Agricultural burning		1.7			5.3	
Organic solvent evaporation		3.1			9.7	
Gasoline marketing		1.2			3.7	
Total	32.0			100.0		

[a]N = Negligible.

Adapted from U.S. Department of Health, Education, and Welfare, *Nationwide Inventory of Air Pollutant Emissions—1968*, p. 13.

similar products. These products consist of 40–80% solvent, which usually evaporates during or after application. The processes involved in the manufacture of these products also constitute potential hydrocarbon sources.

Formation of Photochemical Oxidants

The majority of the harmful effects of hydrocarbon pollution are not caused by the hydrocarbons themselves, but by the products of photochemical reactions in which the hydrocarbons are involved. Hydrocarbons do not readily react with sunlight, but they are reactive toward other substances produced photochemically. The photolytic cycle of NO_2 (Chapter 3) generates several materials with which hydrocarbons readily react. The NO_2 cycle involves the three reactions:

$$NO_2 + \text{Sunlight} \rightarrow NO + O \qquad \text{(eq. 4-1)}$$

$$O + O_2 \rightarrow O_3 \qquad \text{(eq. 4-2)}$$

$$O_3 + NO \rightarrow NO_2 + O_2 \qquad \text{(eq. 4-3)}$$

and the net effect should be a rapid cycling of NO_2. Ozone (O_3) and NO should be formed and destroyed in equal quantities.

The cycle is disrupted when hydrocarbons are present because of their ability to react with either the oxygen atoms (O) produced (equation 4-1) or the ozone produced (equation 4-2). The most likely reaction is that between O and hydrocarbons, because it proceeds 10^8 times faster than the one between O_3 and hydrocarbons. The reaction between O and O_2 is faster than that between oxygen atoms and hydrocarbons, but the latter reaction still proceeds fast enough to upset the cycle.

The product of a reaction between O and a hydrocarbon is a very reactive intermediate species called a hydrocarbon free radical (RO_2). Free radicals of this type can further react with a number of different species including NO, NO_2, O_2, O_3, and other hydrocarbons. Many details are lacking concerning these reactions but some general facts are known.

1. The free radicals react rapidly with NO to produce NO_2. The consequence of this is that with NO removed from the cycle, the normal mechanism for O_3 removal (equation 4-3) has been eliminated, and the concentration of O_3 in the air increases.

2. The free radicals can react with O_2 and NO_2 to give peroxyacylnitrates (PAN).

3. The free radicals can react with other hydrocarbons and oxygen species to produce additional undesirable organic compounds.

These interactions, resulting from the disruption of the NO_2 photolytic cycle by hydrocarbons, are shown in Fig. 4-1.

The mixture of products resulting from the hydrocarbon interference in the NO_2 photolytic cycle is called photochemical smog. It consists of accumulated O_3, CO, PAN, and other organic compounds, including aldehydes, ketones, and alkyl nitrates.

There is a wide variation in the tendency for different hydrocarbons to enter into the photochemical air pollution process. As a consequence, it is impossible to predict accurately, on the basis of total hydrocarbon concentration, the contribution of a hydrocarbon mixture to photochemical air pollution. The detailed composition of the mixture must be known. For example, methane is often more abundant in air than all other hydrocarbons combined. However, it is virtually inert and contributes little toward the formation of photochemical oxidants. Thus a high level of hydrocarbons, consisting mainly of methane, could provide fewer problems than a lower level containing mainly other types.

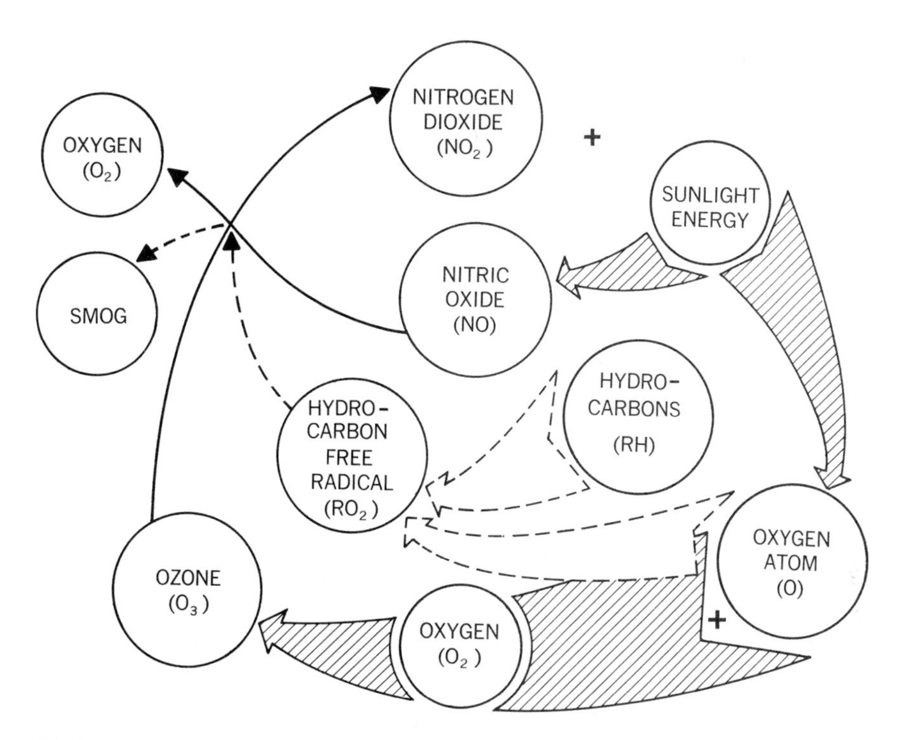

FIGURE 4-1 PHOTOLYTIC CYCLE OF NO_2 WITH HYDROCARBON DISRUPTION

Redrawn, with modifications, from U.S. Dept. of Health, Education, and Welfare, *Air Quality Criteria for Photochemical Oxidants*, p. 3-1.

Concentration and Distribution of Hydrocarbons and Photochemical Oxidants

With the exception of methane, the average concentration of hydrocarbons in urban air falls in the range of 0.03–0.10 ppm (Table 4-2). This represents the concentration range of only the most concentrated of the group. Methane is excepted because of its lack of reactivity in photochemical reactions.

Ozone has been identified as the most concentrated component of polluted air with high photochemical oxidant levels. Table 4-4 gives some indication of the concentration ranges of ozone in urban atmospheres: all values are 1-hour averages. The variation of O_3 concentration with time of day is clearly indicated in Fig. 3-2 of the previous chapter.

The concentrations of peroxyacetylnitrate and other higher weight members of the PAN family have not been measured routinely. They have been detected in the polluted atmospheres of several cities. Their formation has been shown to be directly related to atmospheric ozone production and is

TABLE 4-4 URBAN ATMOSPHERIC OZONE LEVELS, 1967–1968

CITY	NUMBER OF DAYS IN THE SURVEY	NUMBER OF DAYS IN WHICH AT LEAST 1 HOURLY AVERAGE EQUALLED OR EXCEEDED			MAXIMUM HOURLY AVERAGE (ppm)
		0.05 ppm	0.1 ppm	0.15 ppm	
Cincinnati	15	7	2	0	0.11
Washington, D.C.	15	3	0	0	0.07
Denver	58	51	11	1	0.16
Los Angeles	18	16	14	5	0.26
Philadelphia	59	47	21	3	0.18

Adapted from U.S. Dept. of Health, Education, and Welfare, *Air Quality Criteria for Photochemical Oxidants*, p. 3-1.

therefore assumed to be present in atmospheres containing high levels of photochemical oxidants.

Measurements taken in the Los Angeles basin (an area of high photochemical levels) by scientists of the Air Pollution Research Center located at the University of California at Riverside provide the data for Fig. 4-2, in which the monthly average of the daily maximum peroxyacetylnitrate concentration is plotted over an entire year. The daily maximums were 1-hour averaged values. On the basis of these data, a PAN concentration (as peroxyacetylnitrate) on the order of 0.01 ppm would be considered above average. Notice the variation in concentration with the time of year. This provides an obvious correlation between PAN concentration and amount of sunlight.

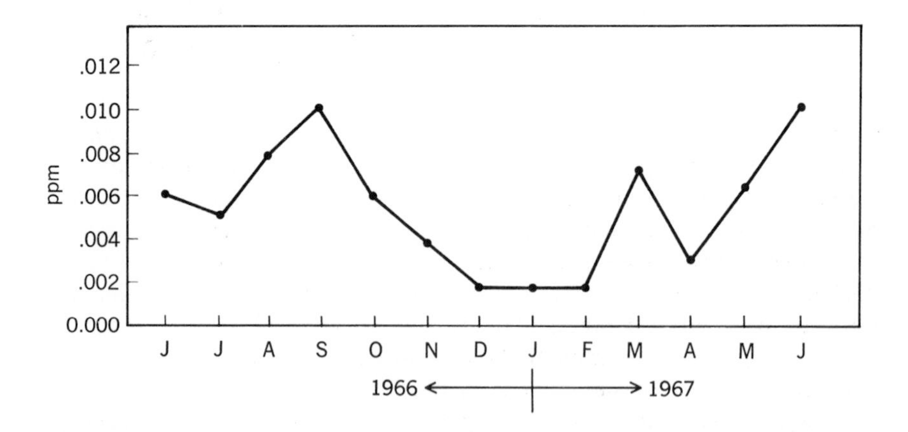

FIGURE 4-2 MONTHLY VARIATION OF PEROXYACETYLNITRATE

Data obtained from U.S. Dept. of Health, Education, and Welfare, *Air Quality Criteria for Photochemical Oxidants*, p. 3-15.

Effects of Hydrocarbons and Photochemical Oxidants on Plants

Injury to vegetation was one of the earliest observed results of photochemical air pollution. Available information suggests that ozone is the most toxic photochemical to plants, but continuing research is uncovering the importance of the PAN family.

A discussion of the individual quantitative effects of ozone and PAN must be limited to laboratory observations and controlled field exposures, because under ambient air conditions, the effects of these compounds cannot be easily differentiated.

The effects of ozone on some particular plants are given in Table 4-5. An important consideration is how closely ambient air ozone levels approach the

TABLE 4-5 TOXIC EFFECTS OF OZONE ON PLANTS

PLANT	OZONE LEVEL (ppm)	EXPOSURE TIME	OBSERVED EFFECTS
Radish	0.05	20 days (8-hr/day)	50% reduction in yield
Carnation	0.07	60 days	50% reduction in floral development
Tobacco	0.10	5.5 hours	50% reduction in pollen germination and pollen tube growth

Data selected from U.S. Dept. of Health, Education, and Welfare, *Air Quality Criteria for Photochemical Oxidants*, p. 6-8.

levels of Table 4-5, which have been demonstrated to affect plants. The information contained in Table 4-4 indicates that, at least in some cities, the levels known to affect plants are being approached. Visible effects of ozone injury to plants are bleached or light flecks or stipples (small clusters of dead cells) on the upper surface of leaves. Fully expanded, mature leaves are most easily damaged. Emergence tip burn, a disease of white pine, puzzled foresters and plant pathologists for years. It has been found that the presence of ozone correlates with the occurrence of this disease.

The other major secondary photochemical pollutant is peroxyacetylnitrate. (In this discussion we shall use the letters PAN for this particular compound. We have previously let PAN represent the entire family of peroxyacylnitrates: the letters PAN are commonly used both ways.) Other common peroxyacylnitrates are peroxypropionylnitrate (PPN), peroxybutyrylnitrate (PBN) and peroxyisobutyrylnitrate ($P_{iso}BN$).

TABLE 4-6 TOXICITY OF SATURATED ALIPHATIC HYDROCARBONS (THROUGH OCTANE)

	CONCENTRATION, ppm											
HYDROCARBONS	100,000	50,000	40,000	30,000	20,000	15,000	10,000	5,000	2,000	1,000	500	0
Methane CH_4	No effect											
Ethane C_2H_6		No effect										
Propane C_3H_8	No irritation noticed; Dizziness in a few min.				Odor not detected		No symptoms after brief exposure					
Butane C_4H_{10}							Drowsiness in 10 min.	Odor not detectable				
Pentane C_5H_{12}	Narcosis in 5–60 min.							Odor readily detectable; No irritation or symptoms in 10 min.		TLV[a]		
Hexane C_6H_{14}			Convulsions and death	Narcosis				Dizziness, giddiness, in 10 min.	No symptoms in 10 min.		TLV[a]	
Heptane C_7H_{16}					Convulsions, death in 30–60 min.	Narcosis in 30–60 min.		In 4 min: marked vertigo, hilarity, incoordination. In 15 min: uncontrolled hilarity or stupor.	Slight vertigo in 4 min.		TLV[a]	
Octane C_8H_8							Narcosis in 30–90 min.				TLV[a]	

[b]TLV–threshold limit value.
Adapted from U.S. Dept. of Health, Education, and Welfare, *Air Quality Criteria for Hydrocarbons*, p. 7-3.

Preliminary studies show that PPN is several times as toxic to plants as PAN, while PBN and $P_{iso}BN$ are still more toxic than PPN. The only member of the family to be extensively studied is PAN. Part of the reason for this is the very low ambient concentrations of PPN and PBN, which are usually present below quantitative detection limits. For this reason, available data are characteristic of PAN.

Plant injury from PAN shows up as a glazing and bronzing of the lower leaf surfaces and a general attack on younger leaves. Eventually, leaf tissue dies. Exposures of a few hours to PAN concentrations of 0.02–0.05 ppm are sufficient to cause injury to vegetation. Five hours of exposure to a PAN level of 0.01 ppm will injure the most sensitive plants. It has been found especially toxic to citrus, forage and salad crops, and coniferous trees.

Ethylene (C_2H_4) is the only hydrocarbon known to have adverse effects on vegetation at ambient concentrations of 1 ppm or less. Acetylene and propylene have shown some toxicity toward plants, but only at concentrations of from 60–500 times as high as that of ethylene. The principal effect of ethylene upon plants is inhibition of growth. It also causes color changes in leaves and death of flowering parts.

Effects of Hydrocarbons and Photochemical Oxidants on Humans

Currently, there is no evidence to indicate that hydrocarbons, at present ambient air concentrations, exert any direct undesirable effects on humans. Experimental data obtained from research on humans and animals indicate that acyclic and alicyclic hydrocarbons produce undesirable effects only at concentrations hundreds to thousands of times higher than those now found in the atmosphere. No effects have been reported for levels lower than 500 ppm. Table 4-6 shows toxicity levels for some saturated acyclic hydrocarbons. Notice the difference between toxicity levels and previously discussed atmospheric levels of hydrocarbons (Table 4-2).

Aromatic hydrocarbons are a greater threat than the acyclic and alicyclic. The vapors are much more irritating to the mucous membranes, and systemic injury can result from the inhalation of aromatic compound vapors. However, no effects have been reported at air concentrations lower than 25 ppm. Some effects of two common aromatics are given in Table 4-7.

Photochemical oxidants enter the body as part of inhaled air and at sublethal concentrations alter, impair, or otherwise interfere with normal respiratory processes. Some eye irritation is also characteristic of exposure to these compounds.

The following effects have been observed in humans exposed to ozone under experimental conditions: in general, no ill effects were noted at concentrations up to 0.2 ppm and a level of about 0.3 ppm appeared to be the threshold level at which nose and throat irritation began. Specifically, exposure to

TABLE 4-7 TOXICITY OF TWO AROMATIC HYDROCARBONS

COMPOUND	CONCENTRATION (ppm)	EFFECT
Benzene C_6H_6	100	Mucous membrane irritation.
	3,000	Endurable ½–1 hour.
	7,500	Dangerous after ½–1 hour.
	20,000	Fatal after 5–10 minutes.
Toluene C_7H_8	200	Mild fatigue, weakness, and confusion after 8 hours.
	600	Loss of coordination, pupils dilated after 8 hours.

Data selected from U.S. Dept. of Health, Education, and Welfare, *Air Quality Criteria for Hydrocarbons*, p. 7-6.

ozone concentrations of 1.0 to 3.0 ppm for a period of 2 hours produced extreme fatigue and lack of coordination in sensitive experimental subjects. Exposure to concentrations of about 9.0 ppm for similar time periods produced severe pulmonary edema in most subjects. A comparison of the above concentrations and those of Table 4-4 lends some perspective to the human health problems of ozone pollution.

It appears that at the concentrations known to occur in ambient atmospheres, PAN (peroxyacetylnitrate) does not present any recognized health hazard. It has been linked to eye irritation, but it appears to play only a minor role. Another member of the family, peroxybenzoylnitrate, more readily causes eye irritation.

Effects of Hydrocarbons and Photochemical Oxidants on Materials

Some researchers feel that much of the degradation of materials now attributed to "weathering" is actually the result of attack by air pollutants, particularly photochemical oxidants. Most of the research in this area up to now has dealt with one oxidant, ozone, and two types of materials, rubber and textiles.

It is known that many organic polymers, including rubber and natural and synthetic textiles, are subject to chemical alteration upon exposure to very small amounts of ozone. Ambient air concentrations are frequently high enough to cause these reactions to take place. The susceptibility to attack increases with increasing numbers of carbon-to-carbon double bonds in the material. The double bond is the site of such attacks.

Two different effects are produced by these reactions, carbon-chain breaking and carbon-chain cross-linking. In the first, the long chains of carbon atoms that make up the polymer are broken, and the material becomes more fluid-like and loses tensile strength. The second effect results in the formation of new links between parallel carbon chains. This causes the material to become less elastic and more brittle. This type of activity takes place in ambient ozone levels much lower than those known to affect humans.

Rubber in a relaxed state can be exposed to ozone for long periods of time without forming any characteristic cracks. However, exposure to ambient concentrations of 0.01–0.02 ppm ozone will result in the formation of cracks if the rubber is under a strain of as little as 2 or 3%. Apparently, rubber is protected by a coating consisting of a compound of rubber and ozone (ozonide) which forms on the surface and protects against further penetration and attack by ozone. This protective film cracks when the rubber is stretched and fresh rubber surfaces are exposed to the atmospheric ozone.

The main use of rubber is in automobile tires, and such rubber is exposed to atmospheric ozone while in a state of continual tensile stress (stretching and flexing). In order to prevent ozone attack and subsequent cracking, antiozonant additives are added to the rubber. These prevent ozone attack but are quite expensive, costing about $0.50 per tire. The total cost of such additives to the tire buyer in 1969 is estimated at about 100 million dollars. Sometimes these substances migrate to the tire surface and lose much of their effectiveness, or they are extracted from the rubber by oil, gasoline, or similar substances. In either case, the tire becomes very susceptible to ozone attack, and cracks result. Table 4-8 shows the effects of ozone on unprotected rubber. The rubber strips were in a state of constant strain by being permanently bent during the experiments.

TABLE 4-8 EFFECTS OF OZONE ON RUBBER

CONCENTRATION OF OZONE (ppm)	TIME FOR FIRST CRACK TO APPEAR (MINUTES)
0.02	65
0.26	5
0.45	3
20,000 (2%)	1 second, cracks formed instantly

Data selected from U.S. Dept. of Health, Education, and Welfare, *Air Quality Criteria for Photochemical Oxidants*, p. 7-3.

Ozone also attacks the cellulose in textile fabrics. Light and humidity appear to be factors necessary before any appreciable alteration takes place in the fiber-breaking strength. The harmful effects of ozone exposure on textiles increases in order for fabrics made of cotton, acetate, nylon, and polyester.

Control of Hydrocarbon and Photochemical Pollutants

Ozone and PAN are secondary pollutants, and their control ultimately depends upon the control of their primary precursors, hydrocarbons and nitrogen oxides. The control of NO_2 pollution was discussed in Chapter 3. This discussion will deal only with control of hydrocarbon emissions.

Four techniques are used to control hydrocarbon emissions from stationary sources. These techniques are incineration, adsorption, absorption, and condensation. Two types of incineration devices are used. The flame afterburner uses a flame to complete the oxidation of hydrocarbons to CO_2 and water. Hydrocarbon removal efficiencies are high in this device. A second device, the catalytic afterburner, makes use of a catalyst to allow the hydrocarbon oxidation to be completed at a lower temperature than in the afterburner. The fuel costs are lower in this type of incinerator, but so are removal efficiencies. The problem of catalyst poisoning (Chapter 2) is also present.

In the adsorption method, exhaust gases are passed through a bed of a granulated adsorber usually consisting of activated carbon. Hydrocarbon vapors are adsorbed onto the surface of the carbon and remain there until they are periodically removed by the passage of steam through the system. The steam and hydrocarbons are then condensed to liquids and the hydrocarbons are recovered for further use.

The absorption method is similar to adsorption, except the exhaust is brought into intimate contact with a liquid in which the hydrocarbons will dissolve or become suspended. The scrubbed exhaust then passes on, leaving the hydrocarbons trapped in the scrubbing liquid. The intimate contact between exhaust gases and absorbing liquid usually takes place in tall columns or scrubbing towers.

The condensation method makes use of the fact that sufficiently low temperatures will cause gaseous hydrocarbons to condense to liquids. The exhaust gases are passed over low temperature surfaces, and the condensed liquid hydrocarbons are left behind and collected.

The control of hydrocarbon emissions from mobile sources (automobiles) is more complicated, for in addition to hydrocarbons in the exhaust, evaporation processes contribute significantly to the problem. The control of evaporative losses was begun on a nationwide basis in 1971. In essence the controls consist of collection systems (a lot of plumbing) which transport fuel vapors from the fuel tank and carburetor to either the crankcase or a cannister full of activated carbon. In either case, the collected vapors are eventually returned to the fuel induction system and burned in the engine.

The removal problem of unburned hydrocarbons from the exhaust is very closely related to the technology previously discussed in the chapters dealing with NO_x and CO, since all three pollutants exist simultaneously in the exhaust. The methods discussed for CO are especially applicable since CO_2 is the desired carbon-containing end product of both CO and hydrocarbon combustion.

$$\text{Hydrocarbons} \xrightarrow{\text{combust}} CO_2 + H_2O \qquad \text{(eq. 4-4)}$$

$$CO \xrightarrow{\text{combust}} CO_2 \qquad \text{(eq. 4-5)}$$

Much effort is currently being expended toward the development of catalytic reactors to solve both the hydrocarbon and CO emission problems.

Suggestions for Further Reading

Journal Articles

1. Leighton, P. A. 1961. *Photochemistry of air pollution.* New York: Academic Press.
2. Stephens, E. R. 1969. The formation, reactions, and properties of peroxyacylnitrates (PANs) in photochemical air. In *Advances in environmental sciences,* vol. 1, ed. Pitts, J. N., and Metcalf, R. L., pp. 119–46. New York: Wiley-Interscience.

Government Documents

1. U.S. Dept. of Health, Education, and Welfare. 1970. *Air quality criteria for hydrocarbons.* National Air Pollution Control Administration Publication No. AP-64.
2. U.S. Dept. of Health, Education, and Welfare. 1970. *Air quality criteria for photochemical oxidants.* National Air Pollution Control Administration Publication No. AP-63.
3. U.S. Dept. of Health, Education, and Welfare. 1970. *Control techniques for carbon monoxide, nitrogen oxide, and hydrocarbon emissions from mobile sources.* National Air Pollution Control Administration Publication No. AP-66.
4. U.S. Dept. of Health, Education, and Welfare. 1970. *Control techniques for hydrocarbon and organic solvent emissions from stationary sources.* National Air Pollution Control Administration Publication No. AP–68.

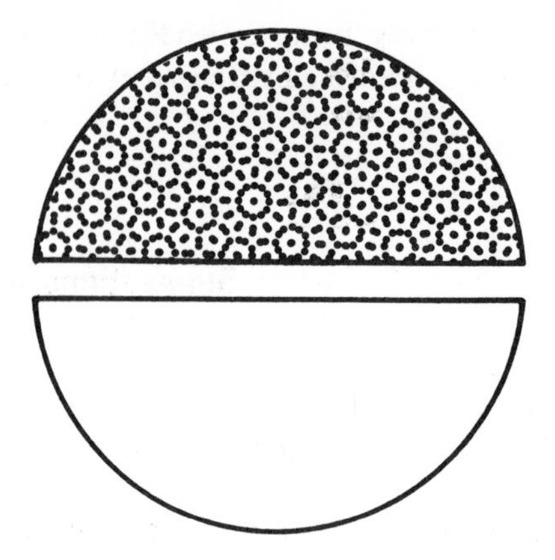

Chapter 5

Sulfur Oxides

Basic Chemical Reactions

Pollution from sulfur oxides consists primarily of two colorless gaseous compounds, sulfur dioxide (SO_2) and sulfur trioxide (SO_3). Collectively, the two are designated SO_x. Sulfur dioxide has a characteristic pungent odor and does not burn in air. Sulfur trioxide is an extremely reactive compound.

The combustion of any sulfur-containing material will produce both sulfur oxides. The relative amount of each one formed does not depend to a large degree upon the amount of oxygen present (unlike the situation encountered with the oxides of carbon). Even in the presence of excess air, SO_2 is formed in the largest amount. The quantity of SO_3 produced is dependent on reaction conditions, especially temperature, and varies between 1% and 10% of the total SO_x.

A simplified mechanism for the formation of SO_x can be represented by a two-step process:

$$S + O_2 \rightleftharpoons SO_2 \qquad \text{(eq. 5-1)}$$

$$2SO_2 + O_2 \rightleftharpoons 2SO_3 \qquad \text{(eq. 5-2)}$$

The small amount of SO_3 generally produced during combustion is the result of two factors, both concerning equation 5-2. The first is the rate at which this reaction proceeds, and the second is the concentration of SO_3 in the equilibrium mixture resulting from this reaction. The reaction proceeds very slowly at relatively low temperatures (200°C for example), but the rate increases with temperature. Therefore, the production of SO_3 is enhanced at high temperatures by the rate factor. The equilibrium mixtures obtained at low temperatures contain higher percentages of SO_3 than mixtures obtained at higher temperatures. Thus, this equilibrium concentration factor favors SO_3 production at lower temperatures.

The reason for the small amount of SO_3 produced now becomes clear: the two factors tend to cancel the effect of each other during combustion. At high temperatures, the reaction establishes equilibrium rapidly because of the high rate, but little SO_3 is present in the mixture. At low temperatures, the reaction proceeds so slowly that the equilibrium condition (with corresponding high SO_3 concentrations) is never established. So SO_3 production is inhibited in the high-temperature combustion zone because of equilibrium conditions. As the products move away from this zone and cool off, equilibrium conditions become favorable, but reaction rates now prevent SO_3 formation in any large quantities.

The existence of SO_3 in the air as a gas is possible only if the concentration of water vapor is very low. When sufficient water vapor is present (normally the case), the SO_3 and water combine immediately to form droplets of sulfuric acid (H_2SO_4) according to the reaction

$$SO_3 + H_2O \rightarrow H_2SO_4 \qquad \text{(eq. 5-3)}$$

Thus H_2SO_4 rather than SO_3 is the compound normally found in the atmosphere. The amount of atmospheric H_2SO_4 is greater than can be justified on the basis of primary SO_3 emissions alone, indicating that other mechanisms must also exist for the production of H_2SO_4.

Once in the atmosphere, SO_2 is partially converted to SO_3 (and then to H_2SO_4) by photolytic and catalytic processes. The amount of SO_2 oxidized to SO_3 depends upon a number of factors including: the amount of moisture present, the intensity, duration and spectral distribution of sunlight, and the amounts of catalytic, sorptive, and alkaline materials present. In daylight and at low humidity, photochemical reactions involving SO_2, NO_2 and hydrocarbons are primarily important in the oxidation. The catalytic effects of nitrogen oxides on SO_2 oxidation are well known and were used for many years in the industrial production of H_2SO_4 by the lead-chamber process. At night and under humid or foggy conditions or during actual rainfall, atmospheric SO_2 is absorbed by alkaline water droplets and reacts at an appreciable rate to form sulfates within the droplets.

Sources of SO_x Pollution

Only about one-third of the sulfur entering the atmosphere, on a world-wide basis, does so as a result of the activities of man, and most of this is in the form of SO_2. The other two-thirds is from natural sources, such as volcanoes, and occurs as the compound H_2S as well as the oxides.

The problem with the man-made pollutants is one of distribution rather than amount. You will recall that this same problem exists with NO_x pollutants. While nature produces two-thirds of the sulfur pollution, it is fairly evenly distributed. The one-third from man-made sources is concentrated, primarily over relatively small urban areas.

Transportation is not the main source of man-made SO_x pollutants. In fact, it accounts for only 2.4% of the total given in Table 5-1. Fuel combustion in stationary sources is the primary culprit in this case, accounting for 73.5% of all man-made SO_x. Of the 24.4 million tons of sulfur oxides making up the 73.5%, 20.1 million tons came from the combustion of coal and 4.3 million from fuel oil use.

TABLE 5-1 NATIONWIDE SULFUR OXIDES EMISSIONS, 1968

SOURCE	EMISSIONS, 10^6 TONS/YR			PERCENTAGE OF TOTAL		
Transportation	0.8			2.4		
Motor vehicles		0.3			0.9	
Gasoline			0.2			0.6
Diesel			0.1			0.3
Aircraft		N[a]			N	
Railroads		0.1			0.3	
Vessels		0.3			0.9	
Nonhighway use of motor fuels		0.1			0.3	
Fuel combustion in stationary sources	24.4			73.5		
Coal		20.1			60.5	
Distillate fuel oil		0.4			1.2	
Residual fuel oil		3.9			11.8	
Natural gas		N			N	
Wood		N			N	
Industrial processes	7.3			22.0		
Solid waste disposal	0.1			0.3		
Miscellaneous	0.6			1.8		
Forest fires		N			N	
Coal refuse		0.6			1.8	
Total	33.2			100.0		

[a]N = Negligible.

Adapted from U.S. Dept. of Health, Education, and Welfare, *Nationwide Inventory of Air Pollutant Emissions—1968*, p. 10.

Sulfur is a common contaminant of both coal and oil, the fossil fuels. Both were formed from once-living materials which contained, in addition to carbon-rich carbohydrates, protein material that contained sulfur. The sulfur survives the fossilizing of the original materials and appears in the resulting fuels as either the element or compounds.

The distribution of SO_x emissions according to the type of stationary source is interesting. Of the 24.4 million tons of SO_x produced, 16.8 million tons came from power plants, 5.1 million tons from industrial plants, and 2.5 million tons from heating devices used in homes and businesses. The 16.8 million tons from power plants (electrical power) account for over half (50.6%) of the total annual SO_x pollution of 33.2 million tons.

Industrial processes rank second to stationary sources with 7.3 million tons or 22.0% of the total. These two sources together account for 95.5% of all SO_x emissions. Four industries account for 7.2 of the 7.3 million tons from industrial processes: smelters contribute 3.9 million tons, petroleum refineries 2.1 million tons, sulfuric acid plants 0.6 million tons, and coking operations 0.6 million tons.

Smelters account for nearly twice the amount of any other industrial process. A reason for this is the natural occurrence of many useful elements in the form of sulfide ores. For example, sulfide ores are important sources of copper ($CuFeS_2$ and Cu_2S), zinc (ZnS), mercury (HgS) and lead (PbS). Most sulfide ores are concentrated and then roasted in air to convert the sulfide into the more readily reduced oxide. In addition, sulfur is a very undesirable impurity in most metals, and it is usually easier and more economical to remove it from the ore rather than from the final metal. Some typical reactions which take place when an ore is roasted are:

$$2ZnS + 3O_2 \rightarrow 2ZnO + 2SO_2 \qquad \text{(eq. 5-4)}$$

$$2PbS + 3O_2 \rightarrow 2PbO + 2SO_2 \qquad \text{(eq. 5-5)}$$

In copper production, the roasting of Cu_2S (copper matte) results in the formation of the metal,

$$Cu_2S + O_2 \rightarrow 2Cu + SO_2 \qquad \text{(eq. 5-6)}$$

Therefore in normal operations, SO_2 is routinely produced as a by-product in metallurgical operations and some of it enters the atmosphere.

Concentration and Distribution of SO_x

In Table 5-2, four different SO_2 concentrations are listed for eight U.S. cities. These are maximum concentrations averaged for the indicated time period and collected between 1962 and 1967. These values will become meaningful when the effects of SO_x pollution are discussed together with the atmospheric concentrations causing the effects.

It was previously mentioned that little SO_3 is present in the atmosphere because of the tendency for combination with water vapor, which results in H_2SO_4 production. Measurements of H_2SO_4 levels along with SO_2 are of interest because of the higher irritant potential of H_2SO_4 and because the ratio of the concentrations of the two helps lead to an understanding of the fate of atmospheric SO_2.

TABLE 5-2 URBAN SO_2 CONCENTRATIONS, 1962–1967

CITY	MAX. CONCENTRATION (ppm) FOR THE TIME PERIOD			
	5 min.	8 hr.	1 day	1 month
Chicago	1.94	1.02	0.79	0.35
Cincinnati	1.15	0.38	0.18	0.06
Denver	0.96	0.14	0.06	0.03
Los Angeles	0.68	0.13	0.10	0.03
Philadelphia	1.25	0.71	0.46	0.15
St. Louis	1.42	0.36	0.26	0.08
San Francisco	0.33	0.10	0.08	0.03
Washington, D.C.	0.87	0.35	0.25	0.11

Data selected from U.S. Dept. of Health, Education, and Welfare, *Air Quality Criteria for Sulfur Oxides*, p. 34.

The results of such measurements indicate that the ratio of H_2SO_4 to SO_2 is dependent on a number of factors including:

1. The amount of moisture in the air.
2. The time the sulfur contaminants have been in the air.
3. The amount of catalytic particulate matter present in the air.
4. The amount of sunlight.
5. The amount of precipitation.

The H_2SO_4:SO_2 ratios found in a 1961 winter study conducted in Los Angeles were found to fall in the range of 0.032–0.246. These ratios are in the same range of values reported by other investigators in other locations. The significance of the values is illustrated by Fig. 5-1.

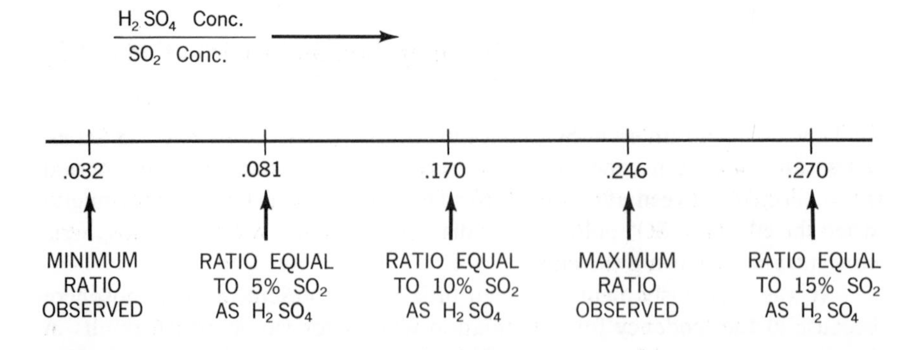

FIGURE 5-1 RANGE OF H_2SO_4/SO_2 RATIO

Effects of SO_x on Plants

Plants are injured by SO_2 in one of two ways, depending on SO_2 concentrations and the duration of exposure. Acute injury, the result of short-term exposures to high SO_2 concentrations, is characterized by dead areas of leaves which dry out and usually bleach to a light tan or ivory color. Exposure to lower concentrations for longer time periods causes chronic injury characterized by a gradual yellowing of the leaves, which is caused by an impedance of the chlorophyll-making mechanism.

Acute injury to plants is related to the plant's ability to transform absorbed SO_2 into H_2SO_4 and then into sulfates. These salts are deposited at the tips or edges of the leaves. The sulfate formed in the leaf is added to that absorbed through the roots, and when sufficiently high levels accumulate, chronic symptoms, accompanied by leaf dropping, occur.

Plants vary widely from species to species in their susceptibility to SO_2 injury. Even within a species, variations occur because of environmental conditions such as temperature, soil moisture, nutrient level, and so forth. The SO_2 concentrations given in Table 5-3 are typical of those that can cause injury to trees and shrubs. These data were obtained from fumigation experiments carried out under prevailing climatic conditions. The trees listed are considered

TABLE 5-3 INJURIOUS LEVELS OF SO_2 TO TREES

TYPE OF TREE	CONCENTRATION OF SO_2 AND TIME TO PRODUCE INJURY	
Pear	0.48 ppm	6 hours
Apple	0.48 ppm	6 hours
Mountain ash	0.54 ppm	3 hours
Ponderosa pine	0.5 ppm	7 hours

Data selected from U.S. Dept. of Health, Education, and Welfare, *Air Quality Criteria for Sulfur Oxides*, p. 64.

to be among the most sensitive to SO_2. A comparison of SO_2 levels from Table 5-2 with those of Table 5-3 indicate that levels of SO_2 high enough to cause plant injury do occur in some urban areas for 8-hour periods.

Damage to plants is especially obvious in areas surrounding large industrial sources of the gas. Studies conducted in the vicinity of a smelter at Trial, British Columbia, discovered plant injury as much as 52 miles away. Three zones of plant injury were determined on the basis of percentage injury to Ponderosa pine. In zone 1, extending 30 miles out from the smelter, 60–100% of the pines were damaged. In zone 2, 30–52 miles from the smelter, 30–60% injury was found; and in zone 3, 52 miles and beyond, 1–30% of the pines suffered some damage.

There is also some evidence that SO_2 might suppress the growth and yield of plants without causing visible injury.

Sulfuric acid mists, another form of SO_x pollution, also damage leaves. A spotted injury results when acid droplets contact leaves already wet from fog or dew.

Effects of SO_x on Humans

The levels of SO_x pollution necessary to produce detectable effects in animals and healthy humans are much higher than levels causing plant damage. In Table 5-4, the effects of some SO_2 concentrations are given. Remember that damage to plants occurs at concentrations of about 0.5 ppm.

TABLE 5-4 EFFECTS OF SO_2 ON HUMANS

CONCENTRATION ppm	EFFECT
3–5	Least amount detectable by odor.
8–12	Least amount causing immediate throat irritation.
20	Least amount causing immediate eye irritation.
20	Least amount causing immediate coughing.
20	Maximum allowable for prolonged exposure.
50–100	Maximum allowable for short (30 min) exposure.
400–500	Dangerous for even short exposures.

Redrawn, with permission, from table in "Physiological Effects of Sulfur Dioxide Gas," from R. E. Kirk and D. F. Othmer, eds., *Encyclopedia of Chemical Technology*, 2nd ed., Vol. 19, p. 417 (New York: John Wiley & Sons, Inc., Copyright © 1969).

The main effect of SO_x pollutants appears to be irritation of the respiratory system. Laboratory observations show that most individuals experience such irritation at SO_2 concentrations of 5 ppm and above. Some sensitive individuals first suffer irritation at 1–2 ppm and, on occasion, have had attacks of severe bronchial spasms upon exposure to SO_2 in the 5–10 ppm range. An indication of the irritation in humans is constriction of the air pathways with corresponding increases in resistance to air flow during breathing.

In a series of experiments dealing with human responses to SO_2, 11 healthy adults were exposed on separate occasions to average SO_2 concentrations of 1, 5, and 13 ppm for 10–30 minutes. The results were:

1. At 1 ppm levels, only 1 of the 11 subjects showed a statistically significant increase in air-flow resistance during breathing.
2. At 5 ppm levels, 9 of the 11 subjects showed a statistically significant increase in air-flow resistance. The average increase was 39% above values obtained from a control group.
3. At 13 ppm levels, all subjects showed an increase in resistance. The average increase was 72% above the control group.

All of the air-flow increases found in the study were reversible upon discontinuation of the SO_2 exposure. In order to put these results into proper perspective, it must be noted that a normal, healthy adult would suffer no marked physiological consequences with an increase in air-flow resistance as high as 300%. There is no evidence that continued exposure to SO_2 at ambient air concentrations produces any cumulative effects, and no definite evidence that SO_2 causes respiratory diseases in healthy people. Cases of severe SO_2 exposure are rare because the gas is so strongly irritating that it serves as its own warning agent at very low concentrations.

In spite of the high levels of SO_2 needed to produce injurious effects in healthy adults, many health authorities consider SO_2 to be the most serious single air pollutant health hazard. The reason for this is not the way SO_2 affects the general population, but the way it affects certain segments of the population, specifically the aged and those who suffer from chronic diseases of the respiratory and cardiovascular systems. These individuals are highly susceptible to prolonged exposure to SO_2 at elevated levels characteristic of air pollution episodes. High SO_2 levels (to 0.2 ppm or greater) have been associated with increases in symptoms among the chronically ill, emergency admissions to hospitals, calls to physicians, certified absences from work, and mortality rates. A three-month study (October–December, 1967) carried out in Chicago on 51 people (average age 57)—all suffering from chronic bronchitis—showed that as the atmospheric SO_2 level increased from 0.1 to 0.2 ppm, the subjects suffered from increased coughing, breathing difficulties, and the formation of purulent sputum.

Striking mortality effects have been observed in association with exceptional episodes of air pollution. In London, an increase in the death rate has been detected when the concentration of SO_2 rises above 0.25 ppm in the presence of smoke. The graphs in Fig. 5-2 (see following page) illustrate the increase in death rate that accompanied the London "killer" smog episodes of January 1956 and December 1957. The SO_2 levels reached approximately 0.4 ppm in each episode. Notice the large fraction of the deaths occurring in the age group of 70+ years.

Although sulfuric acid is a much more potent irritant to man than SO_2, insufficient data are available for a quantitative assessment of it as a health hazard.

Effects of SO_x on Materials

Much of the damage to materials from SO_x pollution is caused by the highly reactive sulfuric acid that is produced when SO_3 reacts with atmospheric water vapor.

The drying and hardening time of some paints is increased upon exposure to SO_2. Exposure of linseed-oil paint films to 1–2 ppm SO_2 increased drying times 50–100%. Some paint films become softer and some more brittle when dried in the presence of SO_2. Such changes in paint films are likely to influence their subsequent durability.

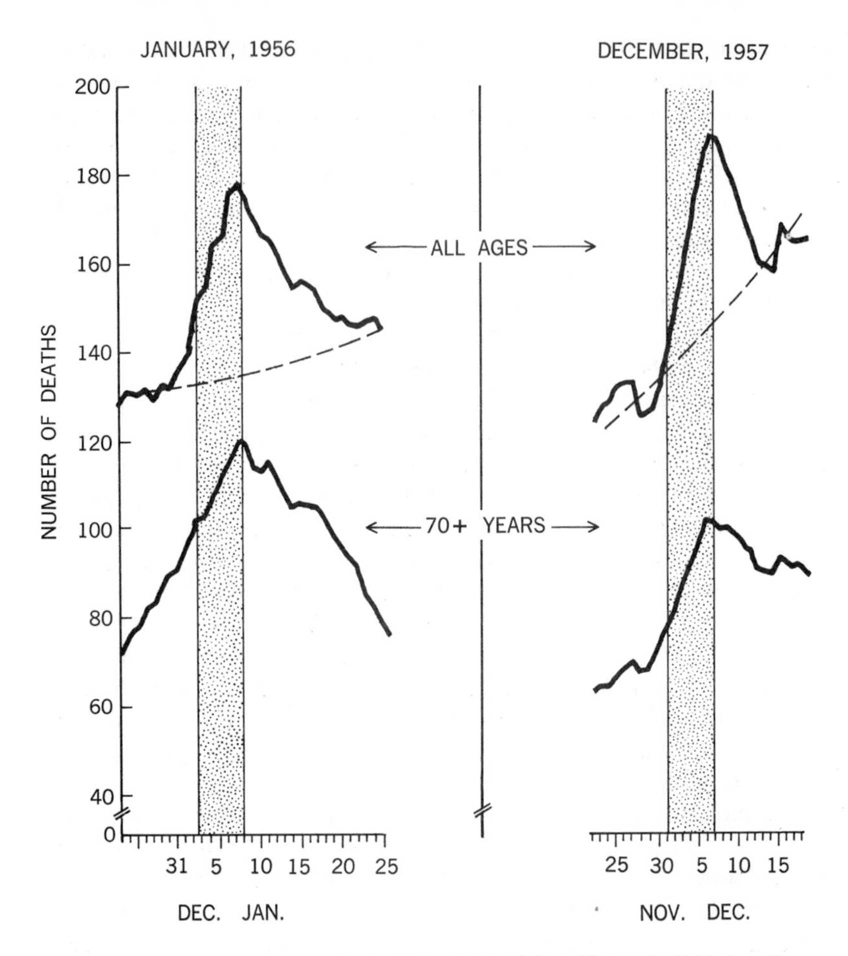

FIGURE 5-2 MORTALITY FIGURES FOR THE JANUARY 1956 AND DECEMBER 1957 SMOG "EPISODES" IN LONDON

The figure shows the increase in numbers of deaths during smog "episodes" (shaded periods), especially in the older age group.

Redrawn, with modifications, from U.S. Dept. of Health, Education, and Welfare, *Air Quality Criteria for Sulfur Oxides*, p. 121.

Corrosion rates of most metals, and especially iron, steel, and zinc, are accelerated by SO_2 polluted environments. Particulate matter, high humidity, and temperature also play important roles in this corrosion. The following correlations, related to metal corrosion, have been found:

1. Increased corrosion rates occur in industrial areas.
2. Corrosion rates are higher in the fall and winter seasons, when particulate and sulfur oxide pollutants are more concentrated because of fuel combustion used for heating.
3. In Pittsburgh from 1926 to 1960, annual SO_2 levels were reduced from

0.15 to 0.05 ppm. Zinc corrosion rates showed a four-fold decrease in the same time period.

4. Studies conducted on mild steel panels exposed to the atmosphere at a number of sites in Chicago showed a high correlation between corrosion rate (measured by weight loss) and atmospheric SO_2 concentrations. Figure 5-3 shows these correlations.

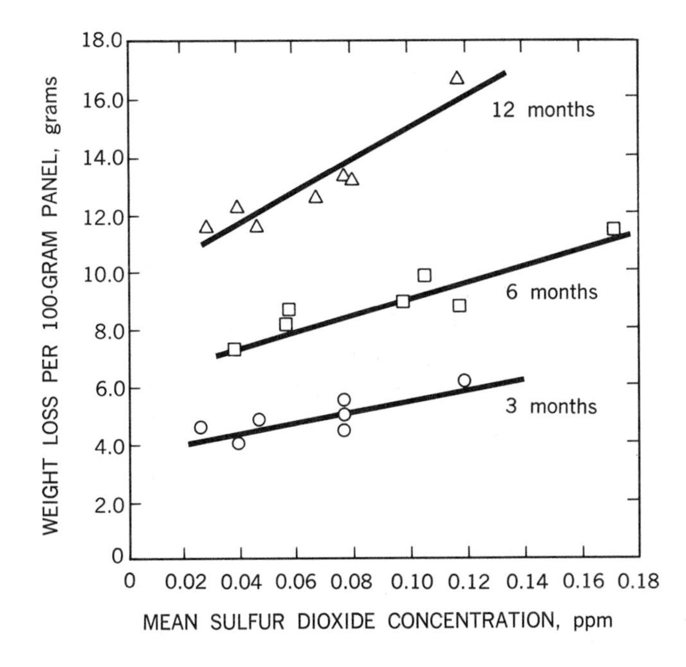

FIGURE 5-3 Reationship Between Corrosion of Mild Steel and Corresponding Mean Sulphur Dioxide Concentration for 3-, 6-, and 12-month Exposures at Seven Chicago Sites (Sept. 1963–1964)

Redrawn from U.S. Dept. of Health, Education, and Welfare, *Air Quality Criteria for Sulfur Oxides*, p. 53.

High concentrations of sulfuric acid from atmospheric pollution are capable of attacking a wide variety of building materials. Especially susceptible are such carbonate-containing substances as marble, limestone, roofing slate, and mortar. The carbonates in these materials are converted to sulfates which are water soluble. The material becomes pitted and weakened mechanically as the soluble sulfates are leached away by rainwater. The reaction is:

$$CaCO_3 \text{ (limestone)} + H_2SO_4 \rightarrow CaSO_4 + CO_2 + H_2O \quad \text{(eq. 5-7)}$$

The calcium sulfate formed on the surface of masonry is about twice as bulky as the carbonate of the stone from which it was formed. Such stone appears "leprous" or "diseased."

Some textile fibers, particularly those from vegetable sources, lose strength when exposed to acids. Animal fibers such as wool are more resistant. Leather has a strong affinity for SO_2, which causes it to lose much of its strength and finally disintegrate. Paper also absorbs SO_2, which is then oxidized to H_2SO_4 causing the paper to discolor and become brittle and fragile.

Control of SO_x Pollution

Possible methods for the reduction and control of SO_x emissions include:

1. The use of low-sulfur fuels.
2. The substitution of other energy sources for fuel combustion.
3. The removal of sulfur from fuel before burning.
4. The removal of SO_x from flue gases.

Certain aspects of each technique support its application, while others discourage it.

The use of low-sulfur fuels is supported by the fact that they are available. They are, however, more costly than higher-sulfur fuels. The total sulfur content of coal ranges between negligible amounts and about 7% by weight. Coal now being mined in the U.S. averages about 2.7% sulfur, and the forecast is that this average will increase to 3.5% by the year 2000. Estimates indicate that about two-thirds of the total U.S. coal reserves consist of the low-sulfur (1.0% or less) variety. However, more than half of this is low-rank coal (giving up about 7000 Btu/lb burned, vs. 12,500 Btu/lb of high-rank burned). Most of this low-sulfur coal is also west of the Mississippi river and generally well removed from population centers. The increased cost over high-sulfur fuels is therefore a result of heat content and especially transportation costs.

Fuel oil combustion accounts for 13% of all SO_x emissions, and again we are confronted with the problem of high vs. low sulfur content. Fuel oils are classified into two categories: distillates (vaporized and condensed), and residuals (left in the boiler during vaporization of others). During refining, the distillates are boiled out of the residual mixture and tend to leave the sulfur behind them. The sulfur tends to concentrate in the residuals. The sulfur content of distillates is 0.04–0.35% by weight. This material is obviously a good low-sulfur fuel, but it costs more than coal and is of limited availability.

Natural gas has low sulfur content, but the reserves are limited and economic factors enter when shipping is considered.

The substitution of energy sources is another technique which seems to present an answer to the SO_x problem, but lack of resources and technological advances limit its application. Hydroelectric plants require no fuel and are certainly free of SO_x pollution. These plants account for 18% of the electric power now produced in the U.S., but this will drop to 13% by 1980. The problem with this approach is the lack of suitable sites for construction of such facilities.

The use of nuclear power to generate electricity could virtually eliminate

SO_x pollution from power plants. In 1970 about 1% of the total electricity was of nuclear power plant origin. By 1980 this will be 22%; and by the year 2000, it is estimated that 50% of all electrical power will be produced by nuclear plants. The fuels for these plants are in limited supply and the technology for development of fast breeder reactors, which could produce additional fuels on a commercial scale, is 15–20 years away.

The removal of sulfur from fuels before burning requires a variety of approaches to handle the various types of fuel and the forms of sulfur they contain. Sulfur occurs in three forms: pyrites, organic compounds, and sulfates. Sulfates are usually present only in small amounts and are not usually regarded as a problem. Organic sulfur is bound in molecules which are part of the coal, and it cannot be removed without chemically changing the nature of the coal itself through processes like carbonizing, liquefaction, or gasification. Pyritic sulfur, present as separate particles, can be removed by physical techniques such as fine grinding followed by washing. These physical methods can cut the pyrite sulfur content of coal by one-half in a single operation, but this is not sufficient for high-sulfur coal (4–2% for example), and multiple treatments are costly.

Much research has gone into the process of converting coal to gas. At the present time pipeline quality low-sulfur gas from coal is possible at a cost approaching that of imported liquefied natural gas. In one gasification process, powdered coal is reacted with steam and oxygen in a fluidized bed at a pressure of 600 to 1000 psi. The product of the reaction is a mixture of CH_4, H_2, CO, H_2S, and CO_2. The CO_2 and H_2S are removed and the remaining CO and H_2 are reacted together to form more CH_4. In a similar process, air is used instead of elemental oxygen.

Processes for the removal of sulfur from residual fuel oils are also receiving attention, and some of these processes are being put into operation in the petroleum industry. An added step in refining reduces the sulfur content of the fuel oil from an average of 2.6% to less than 1.0%. The added step will cause a price increase of 20–35% for the oil.

The removal of SO_2 from flue gases is receiving most of the attention in the battle against SO_x pollution. No method has yet proved satisfactory enough to find widespread use. One process, hopefully of value in power plants, involves the injection of limestone into the combustion zone of the furnace. The limestone reacts with SO_2 according to the equation

$$2CaCO_3 + 2SO_2 + O_2 \rightarrow CaSO_4 + CO_2 \qquad \text{(eq. 5-8)}$$

Removal efficiencies of up to 90% are obtained with the addition of a system which scrubs the flue gas by passing it through a slurry of milk of lime. The primary disadvantage of the system is the large amount of waste material (solid $CaSO_4$, unreacted limestone and fly ash) which must be disposed.

Another recently developed process makes use of a reaction between bisulfite ions (from SO_2) and citrate ions. Flue gas is cooled to 50°C or lower and cleansed of particulates and traces of H_2SO_4. It is then passed into an absorption tower and brought into contact with a solution containing citrate ions. The following reactions take place:

$$SO_2 + H_2O \rightleftharpoons HSO_3^- \text{ (bisulfite ion)} + H^+ \qquad \text{(eq. 5-9)}$$

$$HSO_3^- + H_3Cit^- \text{ (citrate ion)} \rightleftharpoons [(HSO_3 \cdot H_3Cit)^{-2}] \qquad \text{(eq. 5-10)}$$

The solution, now containing the bisulfite-citrate complex $[(HSO_3 \cdot H_3Cit)^{-2}]$, is passed into a closed vessel into which hydrogen sulfide is bubbled. Sulfur precipitates out and is later melted and removed from the solution. The reaction is:

$$(HSO_3 \cdot H_3Cit)^{-2} + H^+ + 2H_2S \rightarrow 3S + H_3Cit^- + 3H_2O \qquad \text{(eq. 5-11)}$$

The regenerated citrate solution is recirculated for further SO_2 removal, and part of the precipitated sulfur is converted to the H_2S used in the process. As much as 99% of flue-gas SO_2 has been removed by the use of this method. The recovered sulfur has a remarkably high purity of 99.99%.

The smelting industry has made some progress toward removing SO_x pollution from the atmosphere. Catalytic oxidation methods are being used to convert SO_2 gas into moderately strong (75–80%) solutions of sulfuric acid. The gas is passed over a catalyst and through a series of condensers to produce the acid. About one-half of the smelters in the U.S. are using this process, but the major problem they face is disposal. In some smelter operations the resulting acid can be used internally, but in others the acid must be marketed; and since most smelters are located in remote areas, transportation costs preclude competitive prices for the acid.

Suggestions for Further Reading

Journal Articles

1. Squires, A. M. 1970. Clean power from coal. *Science* 169:821–28.
2. SO_2 from smelters. 1970. *Environmental Science and Technology* 4:554–68.

Government Documents

1. U.S. Dept. of Commerce. 1971. *Air pollution by sulfur oxides.* Staff Report, National Industrial Pollution Control Council.
2. U.S. Dept. of Health, Education, and Welfare. 1969. *Air quality criteria for sulfur oxides.* National Air Pollution Control Administration Publication No. AP–50.
3. U.S. Dept. of Health, Education, and Welfare, 1969. *Control techniques for sulfur oxide air pollutants.* National Air Pollution Control Administration Publication No. AP–52.

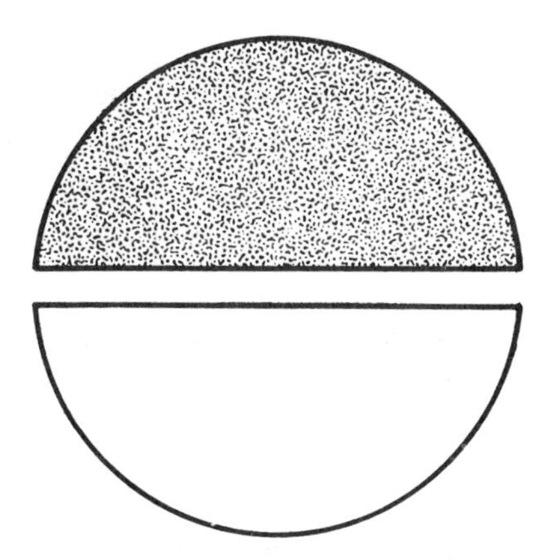

Chapter 6

Particulates

Introduction and General Properties

Although the air pollutants discussed in the previous four chapters have all been gases, it should not be assumed that all air pollutants are in the gaseous state. Small solid particles and liquid droplets, collectively called particulates, are also present in the air in great numbers, and at times they constitute a serious pollution problem.

Many different chemical substances can enter the atmosphere in particulate form. The wide range in chemical composition of products from a single source, coal combustion, is shown in Table 6-1. The values given are the extremes found in fly ash emissions from a variety of coal combustion units.

TABLE 6-1 FLY ASH COMPOSITION (COAL COMBUSTION)

COMPONENT (% CALCULATED AS)	PERCENTAGE OF FLY ASH
Carbon	0.37–36.2
Iron (as Fe_2O_3 or Fe_3O_4)	2.0 –26.8
Magnesium (as MgO)	0.06– 4.77
Calcium (as CaO)	0.12–14.73
Aluminum (as Al_2O_3)	9.81–58.4
Sulfur (as SO_2)	0.12–24.33
Titanium (as TiO_2)	0 – 2.8
Carbonate (as $CO_3^{=}$)	0 – 2.6
Silicon (as SiO_2)	17.3 –63.6
Phosphorus (as P_2O_5)	0.07–47.2
Potassium (as K_2O)	2.8 – 3.0
Sodium (as Na_2O)	0.2 – 0.9
Undetermined	0.08–18.9

Adapted from U.S. Dept. of Health, Education, and Welfare, *Air Quality Criteria for Particulate Matter*, p. 27.

Because of the large variety of substances encountered, a general discussion of chemical properties cannot be made for particulate pollutants. The chemical properties of selected ones will be discussed in various parts of this chapter.

A number of physical properties apply to particulates in general. The most important of these is size, which ranges from a diameter of 0.0002 μ (about the size of a small molecule) to a diameter of about 500 μ. The micron (μ) is a commonly used unit in particulate pollution work and is equal to 10^{-6} meters. Table 6-2 shows the range of sizes possessed by airborne particulates. (Notice the area in the lower right which gives reference sizes and the range visible to the eye.)

In the size ranges given above, particles have a lifetime in the suspended state of something between a few seconds and several months. This lifetime

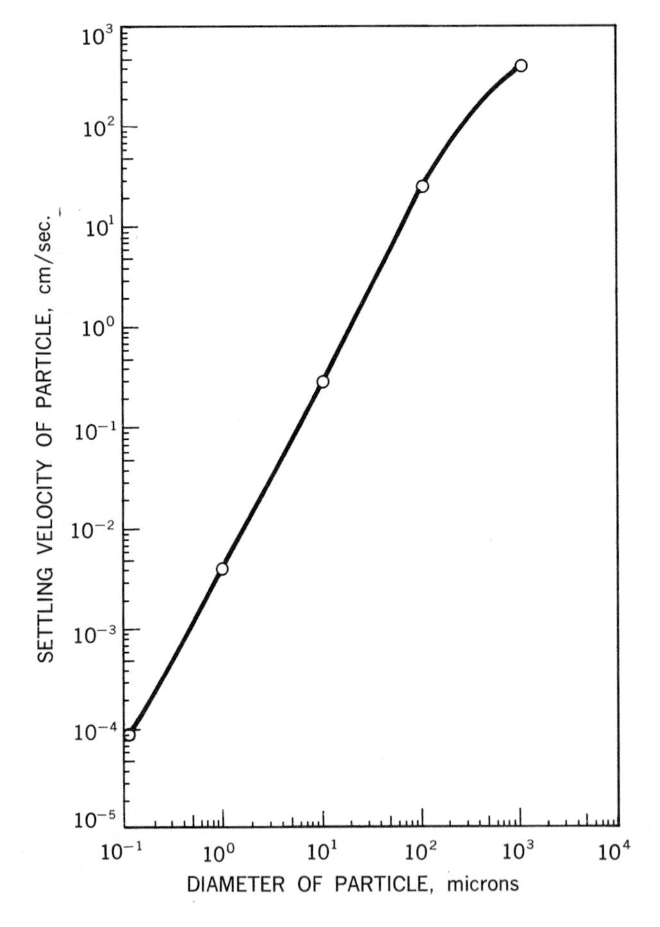

FIGURE 6-1 Settling Velocities in Still Air at 0° C and 760 mm Pressure for Particles Having a Density of 1 g/cm³ as a Function of Particle Diameter

Redrawn from U.S. Dept. of Health, Education, and Welfare, *Air Quality Criteria for Particulate Matter*, p. 7.

TABLE 6-2 SIZES OF AIRBORNE PARTICULATES

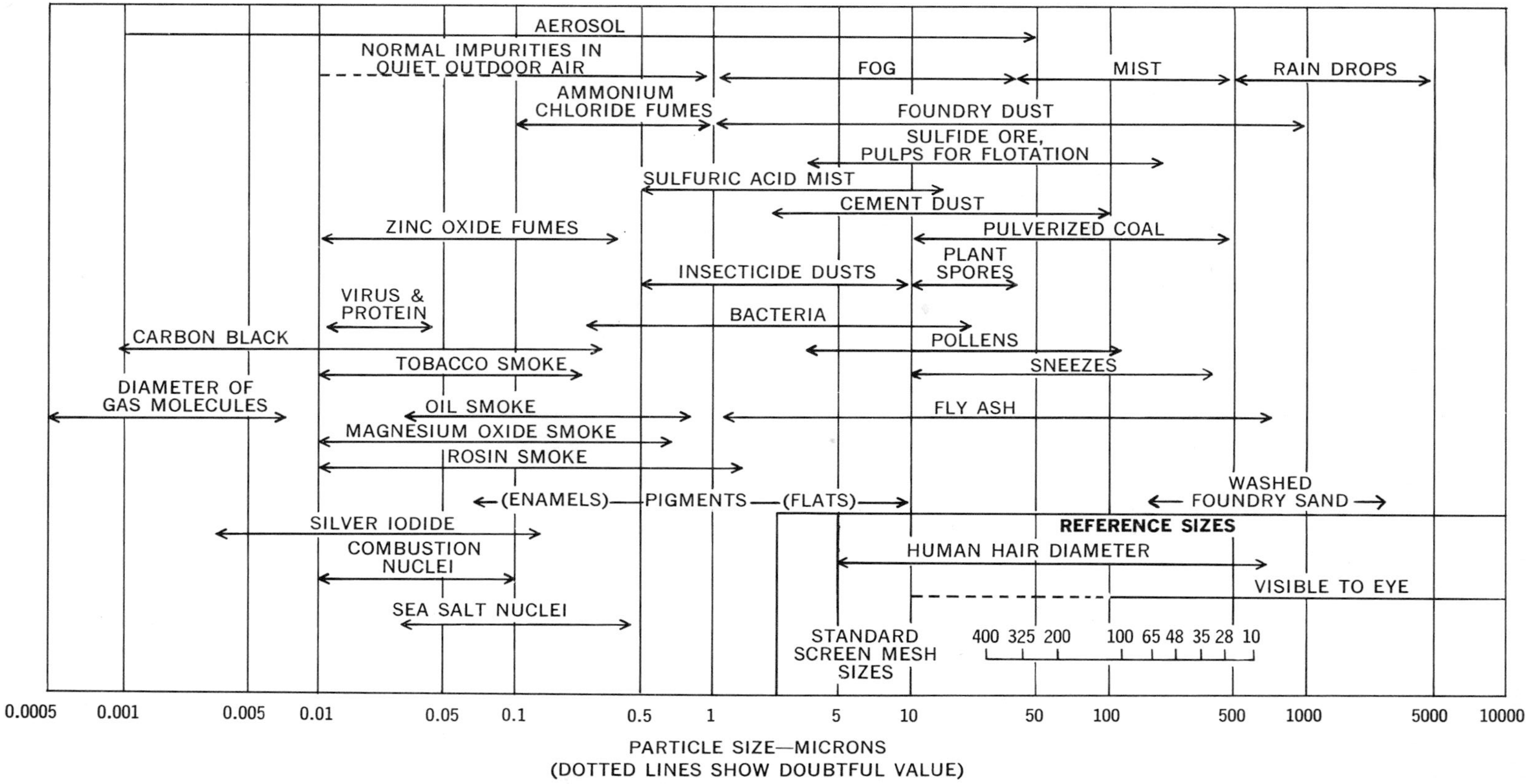

AEROSOL
NORMAL IMPURITIES IN QUIET OUTDOOR AIR
FOG
MIST
RAIN DROPS
AMMONIUM CHLORIDE FUMES
FOUNDRY DUST
SULFIDE ORE, PULPS FOR FLOTATION
SULFURIC ACID MIST
CEMENT DUST
ZINC OXIDE FUMES
PULVERIZED COAL
INSECTICIDE DUSTS
PLANT SPORES
VIRUS & PROTEIN
BACTERIA
CARBON BLACK
POLLENS
TOBACCO SMOKE
SNEEZES
DIAMETER OF GAS MOLECULES
OIL SMOKE
FLY ASH
MAGNESIUM OXIDE SMOKE
ROSIN SMOKE
WASHED FOUNDRY SAND
(ENAMELS)—PIGMENTS—(FLATS)
SILVER IODIDE
COMBUSTION NUCLEI
SEA SALT NUCLEI

REFERENCE SIZES
HUMAN HAIR DIAMETER
VISIBLE TO EYE
STANDARD SCREEN MESH SIZES
400 325 200 100 65 48 35 28 10

0.0005 0.001 0.005 0.01 0.05 0.1 0.5 1 5 10 50 100 500 1000 5000 10000

PARTICLE SIZE—MICRONS
(DOTTED LINES SHOW DOUBTFUL VALUE)

Redrawn, with permission, from L. Byers, "Controlling Atmospheric Particulates," *Technology Tutor* 1:43 (1971).

depends upon the settling rate, which in turn depends upon the size and density of the particles and the turbulence of the air. Figure 6-1 shows the relationship between settling velocity and size of particles assumed to have the same density. These velocities are in still air.

From this figure it is seen that a particle of 0.1 μ diameter settles at a velocity of 8×10^{-5} cm/sec, and one with a diameter of 1000 μ settles at a velocity of 390 cm/sec. A 10,000-fold increase in diameter results in a 4 million-fold increase in settling rate. Particles larger than 2–40 μ (depending on density) do not tend to remain permanently suspended in air but settle out. Even permanently suspended particles have settling rates, but they remain suspended because of air movement.

A second property of particulates is their ability to act as sites for sorption. This property is a function of surface area, which is large for most particulates. The process of sorption takes place when an individual molecule impacts on the surface of a particulate and does not rebound, but sticks or sorbs. The sorption process takes place in three different ways. When the impacting molecule is physically attracted and held to the particulate surface, adsorption has taken place. Chemisorption is the name given to sorption which involves a chemical interaction between the impacting molecule and the particulate surface. If the impacting molecule dissolves into the particulate, it is said to be absorbed. These types of sorption are important in the health effects of particulates.

Optical properties make up the third general property of particulates. Those with diameters below 0.1 μ are sufficiently small, compared to the wavelength of light, that they affect light in a manner similar to molecules and, for example, refract it. Particulates with diameters much greater than 1 μ are so much larger than the wavelength of visible light that they obey the same laws as macroscopic objects and intercept or scatter light roughly in proportion to their cross-sectional areas. These optical properties are important in the determination of effects of atmospheric particulates on solar radiation and visibility. These topics are discussed in detail later in this chapter.

Sources of Particulates

Numerous natural processes inject particulate matter into the atmosphere. Typical of these processes are volcano eruptions and the blowing of dust and soil by the wind. The activities of man also contribute; for example, in the form of dust and asbestos particulates from construction, fly ash from smelters and mining operations, and smoke from incomplete combustion processes.

Some typical statistics concerning man-made particulate pollution are given in Table 6-3. These figures indicate that fuel combustion from stationary sources is responsible for nearly one-third of the total. Industrial processes are second to stationary fuel combustion and also account for nearly one-third of the total.

TABLE 6-3 NATIONWIDE EMISSIONS OF PARTICULATES, 1968

SOURCE	EMISSIONS, 10^6 TONS/YR			PERCENTAGE OF TOTAL		
Transportation	1.2			4.3		
Motor vehicles		0.8			2.8	
Gasoline			0.5			1.8
Diesel			0.3			1.0
Aircraft		N[a]			N	
Railroads		0.2			0.7	
Vessels		0.1			0.4	
Nonhighway use of motor fuels		0.1			0.4	
Fuel combustion in stationary sources	8.9			31.4		
Coal		8.2			29.0	
Fuel oil		0.3			1.0	
Natural gas		0.2			0.7	
Wood		0.2			0.7	
Industrial processes	7.5			26.5		
Solid waste disposal	1.1			3.9		
Miscellaneous	9.6			33.9		
Forest fires		6.7			23.7	
Structural fires		0.1			0.4	
Coal refuse burning		0.4			1.4	
Agricultural burning		2.4			8.4	
Total	28.3			100.0		

[a]N = Negligible.
Adapted from U.S. Dept. of Health, Education, and Welfare, *Nationwide Inventory of Air Pollutant Emissions—1968*, p. 7.

Coal is involved in 92% of the combustion in stationary sources. The variety of particulate pollutants in fly ash from coal combustion was given in Table 6-1. Of the 8.9 million tons of particulates resulting from stationary fuel combustion, power plants were the sources of 5.6 million tons and industries were responsible for 2.6 million tons. A more detailed breakdown of the contributions from industrial processes is given in Table 6-4. It is apparent from these data that iron and steel industries lead the industrial contributors, followed by the sand, stone, rock, and the cement industries. The third largest source is the grain handling and storage industry.

Relationships exist between the size of particulate pollutants and their sources. Particles larger than 10 μ in diameter result from such mechanical processes as wind erosion, grinding and spraying, and the pulverizing of materials by vehicles and pedestrians. Particles between 1–10 μ in diameter usually include local soil, process dusts and combustion products from local industries, and, in appropriate locations, sea salt. Particles between 0.1–1 μ in diameter are primarily combustion products and photochemical aerosols.

TABLE 6-4 PARTICULATE EMISSIONS FROM INDUSTRIAL PROCESSES, 1968 (TONS/YEAR)

INDUSTRY	EMISSIONS
Iron and steel	1,910,000
Other primary metals	40,000
Grey-iron foundries	170,000
Other secondary metals	50,000
Cement	870,000
Stone, sand, rock, etc.	870,000
Coal cleaning	185,000
Phosphate rock	205,000
Lime	450,000
Asphalt batching	540,000
Other mineral products	180,000
Oil refineries	100,000
Other chemical industries	90,000
Grain handling and storage	800,000
Pulp and paper	720,000
Flour and feed milling	320,000
Other	30,000

Adapted from U.S. Dept. of Health, Education, and Welfare, *Nationwide Inventory of Air Pollutant Emissions—1968*, p. 7.

Particles below 0.1 μ diameter have not been extensively identified chemically. They apparently originate almost entirely from combustion sources.

Concentration of Particulates

The units used to express concentrations of particulates are micrograms per cubic meter of air ($\mu g/m^3$). In order to convert from $\mu g/m^3$ to ppm on a volume basis, the molecular weight of the particulate is needed. No acceptable particulate molecular weights are available because of the diverse composition of particulates.

Average suspended particle concentrations, as determined by the National Air Surveillance Network (1957–65), are given in Table 6-5, and specific average values obtained near city centers of various urban areas from 1961–1965 are included in Table 6-6.

TABLE 6-5 TYPICAL PARTICULATE CONCENTRATIONS, 1961–1965

TYPE OF LOCATION	PARTICULATE CONCENTRATION ($\mu g/m^3$)
Remote nonurban area	10
Near urban areas	60
Urban areas	60–220
Heavily polluted areas	up to 2000

Data selected from U.S. Dept. of Health, Education, and Welfare, *Air Quality Criteria for Particulate Matter*, p. 11.

TABLE 6-6 SUSPENDED PARTICLE CONCENTRATIONS (GEOMETRIC MEAN OF CENTER CITY STATION) IN URBAN AREAS, 1961–1965

STANDARD METROPOLITAN STATISTICAL AREA	TOTAL SUSPENDED PARTICLES	
	μg/m³	Rank
Chattanooga	180	1
Chicago–Gary–Hammond–East Chicago	177	2
Philadelphia	170	3
St. Louis	168	4
Canton	165	5
Pittsburgh	163	6
Indianapolis	158	7
Wilmington	154	8
Louisville	152	9
Youngstown	148	10
Denver	147	11
Los Angeles–Long Beach	145.5	12
Detroit	143	13
Baltimore	141	14.5
Birmingham	141	14.5
Kansas City	140	16.5
York	140	16.5
New York–Jersey City–Newark–Passaic–Paterson–Clifton	135	18
Akron	134	20
Boston	134	20
Cleveland	134	20
Cincinnati	133	22.5
Milwaukee	133	22.5
Grand Rapids	131	24
Nashville	128	25
Syracuse	127	26
Buffalo	126	27.5
Reading	126	27.5
Dayton	123	29
Allentown–Bethlehem–Easton	120.5	30
Columbus	113	31.5
Memphis	113	31.5

Adapted from U.S. Dept. of Health, Education, and Welfare, *Air Quality Criteria for Particulate Matter*, p. 13.

Effects of Particulates on Plants

Relatively little research has been done on the effects of particulate pollution on vegetation. Most of what has been done has been concerned with specific dusts rather than the conglomerate mixture usually present in the atmosphere. Studies done in 1966 dealing with cement kiln dust are illustrative of some of the problems related to particulate effects on plants. This dust, when combined with a mist or light rain, formed a thick crust on upper leaf surfaces which would not wash off and could be removed only with force. The encrusted dust was found to interfere with photosynthesis in the plant by shielding out needed sunlight and upsetting the process of CO_2 exchange with the atmosphere. The growth of such plants was inhibited.

A possible indirect effect of particulates deposited on plants is the chance that the particulates might contain chemical components harmful to animals that use the plants as food.

Effects of Particulates on Humans

Particulate pollutants enter the human body almost exclusively by way of the respiratory system, and their most important immediate effects involve this system. Particle size is probably the most important factor to be considered, for it is this factor which determines the extent of penetration into the respiratory system.

The respiratory system has several built-in defenses which prevent particulates, both solid and liquid, from getting to the lungs. Nostril hair filters out larger particulates. Smaller particles are stopped by mucous membranes that line the respiratory system and provide a surface to which the particles adhere. In some parts of the system tiny hairs (cilia) wave back and forth and

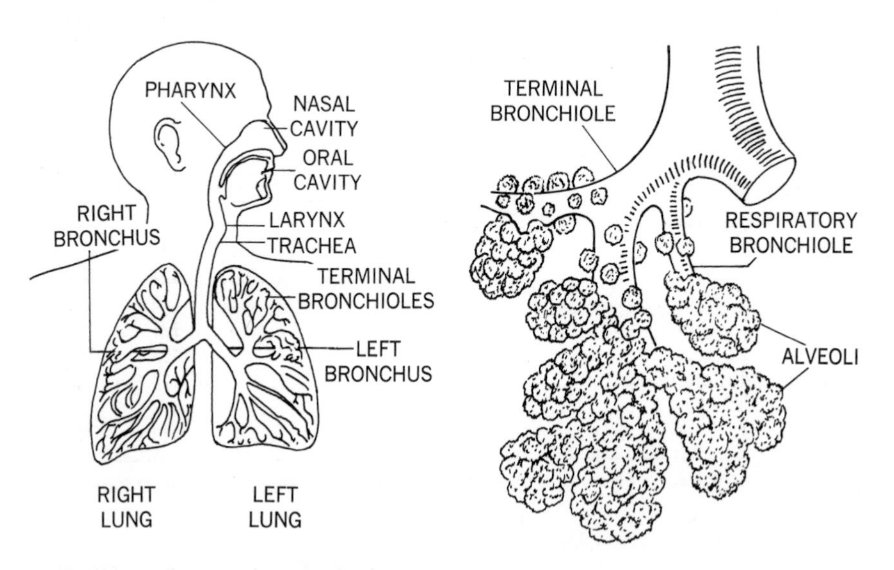

FIGURE 6-2 (A) THE MAJOR ANATOMICAL FEATURES OF THE HUMAN RESPIRATORY SYSTEM

The diagram shows the major divisions of the human respiratory tract into nasopharyngeal, tracheobronchial, and pulmonary compartments.

FIGURE 6-2 (B) THE TERMINAL BRONCHIAL AND ALVEOLAR STRUCTURE OF THE HUMAN LUNG

The diagram shows the pulmonary structure of the respiratory tract.

Redrawn from U.S. Dept. of Health, Education, and Welfare, *Air Quality Criteria for Particulate Matter*, p. 112.

move mucous along in a current that carries trapped particulates out of the respiratory system to the throat, where they are swallowed. The sizes and shapes of air passages effectively block some particulates.

In Fig. 6-2 A and B, the main parts of the respiratory system are given, including a detail of the terminal pulmonary structure with its tiny alveolar (air) sacs. These alveolar sacs, resulting from much branching of the air ducts, are the sites at which oxygen and carbon dioxide are exchanged between the atmosphere and the blood.

Particles over 5.0 μ in diameter are stopped and deposited mainly in the nose and the throat. Those that do penetrate to the lungs do not often go beyond the air ducts or bronchi, and even these are soon removed by ciliary action. Particles ranging in size from 0.5–5.0 μ in diameter can be deposited in the lung as far as the bronchioles. Few reach the alveoli. Most particles deposited in the bronchioles are removed by the cilia within two hours. Particles less than 0.5 μ in diameter reach and may settle in the alveoli. The removal of such particles from these areas is much less rapid and less complete than from the larger passages. Some of the particles retained in the alveoli are absorbed into the blood.

Particulate matter which enters and remains in the lungs can exert a toxic effect in three different ways.

1. The particles may be intrinsically toxic because of chemical or physical characteristics. More will be said later about this type of particle.
2. The particles may be inert themselves but once in the respiratory tract they may interfere with the removal of other more harmful material.
3. The particles may carry adsorbed or absorbed irritating gas molecules and thus enable such molecules to reach and remain in sensitive areas of the lungs. Carbon, in the form of soot, is a common particulate with a very good ability to sorb gas molecules on the surface.

Toxic Particulates

Intrinsically toxic particulates are not commonly found in the atmosphere in high concentrations except for sulfuric acid aerosol, which was discussed in Chapter 5. However, many toxic particles are found in the air in trace amounts. Table 6-7 contains information about a number of trace metals in this category that may pose health hazards in the environment.

Much of the current concern about such substances centers around the possible continued build-up of their concentrations as a result of man's activities. In many cases facts concerning toxic levels and trace particulate transformations in the environment are largely unknown. Intensive research is in progress to uncover this information.

Beryllium and asbestos are examples of airborne particulates that have become matters of concern. In March 1971, the United States Environmental Protection Agency (EPA) announced that both of these pollutants had been added to the list of "hazardous air pollutants." The inclusion of a substance

TABLE 6-7 TRACE METALS THAT MAY POSE HEALTH HAZARDS IN THE ENVIRONMENT

ELEMENT	SOURCES	HEALTH EFFECTS
Nickel	Diesel oil, residual oil, coal, tobacco smoke, chemicals and catalysts, steel and nonferrous alloys	Lung cancer (as carbonyl)
Beryllium	Coal, industry (new uses proposed in nuclear power industry, as rocket fuel)	Acute and chronic system poison, cancer
Boron	Coal, cleaning agents, medicinals, glass making, other industrial	Nontoxic except as borane
Germanium	Coal	Little innate toxicity
Arsenic	Coal, petroleum, detergents, pesticides, mine tailings	Hazard disputed, may cause cancer
Selenium	Coal, sulfur	May cause dental caries, carcinogenic in rats, essential to mammals in low doses
Yttrium	Coal, petroleum	Carcinogenic in mice over long-term exposure
Mercury	Coal, electrical batteries, other industrial	Nerve damage and death
Vanadium	Petroleum (Venezuela, Iran), chemicals and catalysts, steel and nonferrous alloys	Probably no hazard at current levels
Cadmium	Coal, zinc mining, water mains and pipes, tobacco smoke	Cardiovascular disease and hypertension in humans suspected, interferes with zinc and copper metabolism
Antimony	Industry	Shortened life span in rats
Lead	Auto exhaust (from gasoline), paints (prior to about 1948)	Brain damage, convulsions, behavioral disorders, death

Redrawn, with permission, from table in *Chemical and Engineering News* 49:30 (July 19, 1971).

on this list does not mean that current levels in the air are dangerous. It does mean that the release of each substance into the environment should be carefully controlled since slight exposure could threaten human health. The EPA action was prompted by the increasing use and release of these substances into the atmosphere and the possible resultant build-up. The listing amounts to a statement of serious concern about these substances.

The poisonous nature of beryllium and its compounds has been recognized for years. Soluble compounds such as $BeSO_4$ and $BeCl_2$ commonly produce acute inflammation of the lungs. Beryllium metal or insoluble compounds cause the chronic pulmonary disease, berylliosis.

In spite of the poisonous nature of beryllium and its compounds, consumption of beryllium in the United States increased more than 500% in the twenty year period 1948–1968. This increase was due to the desirable physical properties of beryllium. Metallic beryllium has a density only two-thirds that of aluminum, a melting point twice as high as aluminum, and a pound-for-pound strength three times that of steel. Important uses of beryllium include applications in:

1. Missiles and space vehicles—beryllium is used as a structural metal because of the high strength-to-weight ratio and the ability to withstand high temperatures.
2. Alloys—when 2% beryllium is added to copper, an alloy results with increased strength and resistance to corrosion and fatigue.
3. Nuclear Reactors—beryllium absorbs fewer neutrons than any other known structural material. This property plus the high strength-to-weight ratio makes it useful in the structures of reactors.
4. Rocket Fuels—finely powdered metallic beryllium is added to increase the performance of rocket fuels. In addition to being light weight, beryllium releases a large amount of energy upon combining with oxygen.

Air pollution from the first three uses above comes from the manufacturing processes. Cutting, grinding, and similar treatments cause the formation of dusts while fumes (primarily the oxide) result from the condensation of vapors formed during melting, casting, or welding processes. Three hazards are associated with the fourth use listed: contact through the handling of beryllium metal prior to launch, the formation of fumes (oxides) upon firing, and possible accidental fires or explosions.

Coal burning is another source of atmospheric beryllium because most coal contains beryllium as an impurity. The average concentration of beryllium in coal deposits is 1–3 ppm, but concentrations up to 31 ppm have been found.

Table 6-8 gives beryllium exposure limits set by the Atomic Energy Commission (AEC) for various situations, and measured atmospheric beryllium levels.

Recent findings indicate that inhalation of asbestos, a substance used for insulation by the building trade, can produce serious problems in previously healthy lungs. Asbestos is a fibrous silicate mineral that may persist for long periods of time in the environment. The fibers are very brittle and are easily fractured into tiny fibrils so small that 10^{15} of them would weigh no more than 1 g.

TABLE 6-8 BERYLLIUM EXPOSURE LIMITS SET BY THE AEC

AEC EXPOSURE LIMIT ($\mu g/m^3$)	CONDITIONS	MEASURED ATMOSPHERIC LEVELS ($\mu g/m^3$)	CONDITIONS
25	Industrial limit for short-term exposure	0.028–0.083	Concentration in vicinity of a beryllium plant
2	Industrial limit averaged over an eight hour work period	0.008	Maximum ambient air value
0.01	Industrial limit averaged over 30 days for people living in the neighborhood of a beryllium plant	0.0005	Daily average air values

Data for exposure limits from *Environmental Science and Technology* 5:584 (1971); data for ambient air concentrations from U.S. Environmental Protection Agency, "Beryllium and Air Pollution," Air Pollution Control Office Publication AP-83, p. 4.

Individuals engaged in certain occupations are subjected to higher asbestos levels than the general population. Installers of building insulation are in this situation. Asbestos workers involved in such jobs have a higher rate of serious lung disorders than normal. Approximately 1 in 5 deaths, among a New York group of such workers sampled, was found to be caused by lung cancer.

Asbestos has been detected in the lungs of nonconstruction workers as well. Asbestosis bodies were found in 1449 samples of lung tissue removed and studied during 3000 consecutive autopsies performed in New York City during 1968.

Preliminary measurements of the amount of asbestos in air over New York City, Philadelphia, and suburban Ridgewood, New Jersey showed amounts which varied between 0.01–0.1 $\mu g/m^3$. Measurements taken near a construction site in which spray fireproofing with asbestos was used, showed the distribution of airborne asbestos concentrations given in Table 6-9. Further study is needed in this area of air pollution, but it is clear that occupational and, in some cases, local neighborhood exposures to airborne asbestos constitute a health hazard.

TABLE 6-9 DISTRIBUTION OF AIRBORNE ASBESTOS

LOCATION RELATIVE TO SOURCE	CONCENTRATION ($\mu g/m^3$)
Downwind from source	.045–.180
45° from source	.015–.030
Upwind from source	.020

Redrawn, with permission, from table in *Environment* 13:30 (March, 1971).

Effects of Particulates on Materials

Airborne particles, including soot, dust, fumes, and mist, can cause a wide range of damage to materials. The extent and type of damage depend upon the chemical composition and physical state of the pollutant. Passive damage is caused when particulates settle on and soil materials, creating a need for more frequent cleaning. The cleaning processes weaken the materials. Chemical damage results when the particulates themselves are corrosive, or when they carry adsorbed or absorbed corrosive substances along with them.

Metals are generally resistant to corrosion in dry air and even in clean air that contains only small amounts of water. Particulates accelerate corrosion, especially in the presence of sulfur-containing compounds. Part of the function of particulates in accelerating corrosion rates is to serve as nuclei on which moisture can condense. Gases sorbed to the particulates dissolve in the water droplets formed. In most laboratory studies, corrosion rates increased significantly with humidity.

Field experiments show that corrosion rates of various metals are highest in urban and industrial atmospheres. Standardized open hearth iron specimens exhibited strikingly different corrosion rates when exposed to the atmospheres of divers locations throughout the world: those specimens exposed to heavily polluted industrial atmospheres were the most rapidly corroded. The results of these experiments are summarized in Table 6-10.

TABLE 6-10 CORROSION OF OPEN HEARTH IRON SPECIMENS IN DIFFERENT LOCATIONS

LOCATION	TYPE OF ATMOSPHERE	ANNUAL WEIGHT LOSS, g	RELATIVE CORROSIVITY
Khartoum, Sudan	Dry inland	0.16	1
Abisko, North Sweden	Unpolluted	0.46	3
Aro, Nigeria	Tropical inland	1.19	8
Singapore, Malaya	Tropical marine	1.36	9
Basrah, Iran	Dry inland	1.39	9
Apapa, Nigeria	Tropical marine	2.29	15
State College, Pa., USA	Rural	3.75	25
Berlin, Germany	Semi-industrial	4.71	32
Llanwrtyd Wells, British Isles	Semi-marine	5.23	35
Calshot, British Isles	Marine	6.10	41
Sandy Hook, N.J., USA	Marine-semi-industrial	7.34	50
Congella, South Africa	Marine	7.34	50
Motherwell, British Isles	Industrial	8.17	55
Woolwich, British Isles	Industrial	8.91	60
Pittsburgh, Pa., USA	Industrial	9.65	65
Sheffield Univ., British Isles	Industrial	11.53	78
Derby South End, British Isles	Industrial	12.05	81
Derby North End, British Isles	Industrial	12.52	84
Frodingham, British Isles	Industrial	14.81	100

Adapted from U.S. Dept. of Health, Education, and Welfare, *Air Quality Criteria for Particulate Matter*, p. 66.

The ability of particulates to damage and soil buildings, sculpture, and other structures is especially obvious in cities where large amounts of coal and sulfur-bearing oils are used. The resulting particulates are usually tarry, sticky, and acidic so they adhere to surfaces and behave as acid reservoirs for corrosion.

Painted surfaces are very susceptible to particulate damage before the paint is dry. In addition, some particulate fumes and mists react directly with dry painted surfaces, and cause considerable damage. This type of paint damage is common on automobiles frequently parked near industrial plants.

The soiling of textile materials is one of the most important harmful effects from particulates. As mentioned earlier, the resultant increase in cleaning frequency weakens the fabric. The extent of soiling by particulates depends upon the humidity, wind speed, and particulate size. Also, some fabrics easily acquire electrical charges from friction. They then attract particulates carrying charges of the opposite sign and increase the rate of soiling. Some textiles are vulnerable to attack by acidic components of particulate pollution. Textiles in this category are cotton, linen, and rayon.

Effects of Particulates on Solar Radiation and Climate

Particulates in the atmosphere exert a definite influence on the amount and type of solar radiation that reaches the surface of the earth. This influence is the result of light scattering and absorption by the particulates. One principal effect is the reduction of visibility. Light passing from an object to an observer is both absorbed and scattered before it reaches the observer. The intensities of light received from the object and from the background are both diminished. The difference between them is also diminished, resulting in less contrast between the two. The eye has difficulty distinguishing between the object and the background. Decreased visibility creates obvious problems, some dangerous (aircraft or automobile operation) and some just annoying (sightseeing, and so forth). The relationship between particulate concentration and estimated visibility limit is shown in Table 6-11.

TABLE 6-11 EFFECT OF PARTICULATES ON VISIBILITY

CONCENTRATION ($\mu g/m^3$)	VISIBILITY (MILES)	TYPE OF AREA
30	25	Typical rural
100	7.5	Common urban
200	3.75	Common urban
750	1.0	Heavily polluted urban

Data selected from U.S. Dept. of Health, Education, and Welfare, *Air Quality Criteria for Particulate Matter*, pp. 60–61.

Illumination problems are created by particulate pollution. In some cities the processes of scattering and absorption may reduce by one-third or more the amount of visible light reaching the earth's surface. The gloom resulting from reduced amounts of sunlight creates a heavy need for artificial illumination, which in turn requires more power, which could mean that more pollutants from the power plant will be released, and a cycle is created.

The amount of particulate pollution varies with the season. In autumn and winter, increased heating of houses and other buildings creates a demand for more power which causes more particulates. This perhaps accounts in part for gloomy winter days. The data in Table 6-12 show the seasonal variation in illumination reaching the ground in the city of Vienna, Austria, compared to the amounts reaching the ground in a surrounding suburb.

TABLE 6-12 SEASONAL ILLUMINATION VARIATION

SEASON	PERCENTAGE OF SUBURB ILLUMINATION IN CITY
Winter	85
Spring	92
Summer	92
Fall	87

Data selected from U.S. Dept. of Health, Education, and Welfare, *Air Quality Criteria for Particulate Matter*, p. 39.

The climate may be affected in two other ways by particulate pollution. Particulates in the atmosphere may influence the formation of clouds, rain, and snow by acting as nuclei upon which water condensation can take place. Patterns of precipitation over cities and adjacent countrysides show a correlation with atmospheric particulate levels. Louisville, Pittsburgh, and Buffalo show a minimum precipitation rate for Sundays, when particulate levels are usually the lowest. Records covering several decades indicate increased precipitation levels with increased atmospheric pollution.

World-wide climatic changes may also be related to particulate pollution. The reduction in the amount of solar radiation reaching the earth's surface may be upsetting the delicate heat balance of the earth's atmosphere. In spite of an increase in CO_2 content of the atmosphere over the past several decades, which should cause an atmospheric temperature increase (see the greenhouse effect, Chapter 7), the average world-wide temperature has been decreasing slightly since the 1940s. The increased reflection of solar radiation by particulates may be more than compensating for the climatic effect of increased atmospheric CO_2.

Control of Particulate Emissions

Techniques for controlling particulate emissions are all based on capturing them before they enter the atmosphere. The methods used to accomplish this feat are dependent on the size of particulate. Four types of equipment are now in use and are described below.

1. *Gravity settling chamber.* Effluent gases are passed into a chamber which is large enough to allow gas velocities to decrease and provide a residence time sufficient to allow dust or droplets to settle out. The chamber is commonly in the shape of a horizontal rectangular tank. Particles with a diameter greater than 50 μ are generally removed in this way. The longer settling time required for smaller particles causes this type of equipment to be impractical from the point of view of size.

2. *Cyclone Collector.* This device is an application of the fact that a gas flowing in a tight circular spiral produces a centrifugal force on suspended particles, forcing them to move outward through the gas stream to a wall where they are collected. Such units have a 95% removal efficiency for particles in the diameter range of 5–20 μ. Figure 6-3 is a schematic diagram of a typical cyclone collector.

3. *Wet Scrubbers.* Cleaning devices utilizing a liquid (usually water) to assist in removing solid, liquid or gaseous contaminants are called wet scrubbers. The effectiveness of devices of this type depends upon the degree of contact and interaction between the liquid phase and the contaminants to be

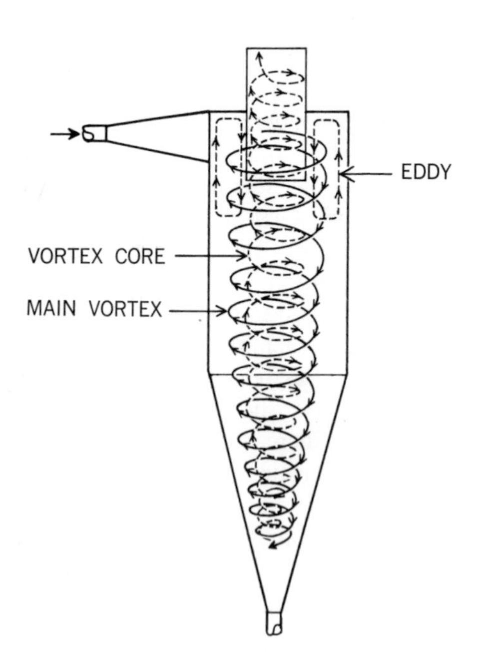

FIGURE 6-3 TYPICAL CYCLONE COLLECTOR
Redrawn from L. Byers, "Controlling Atmospheric Particulates," *Technology Tutor* 1:46 (1971).

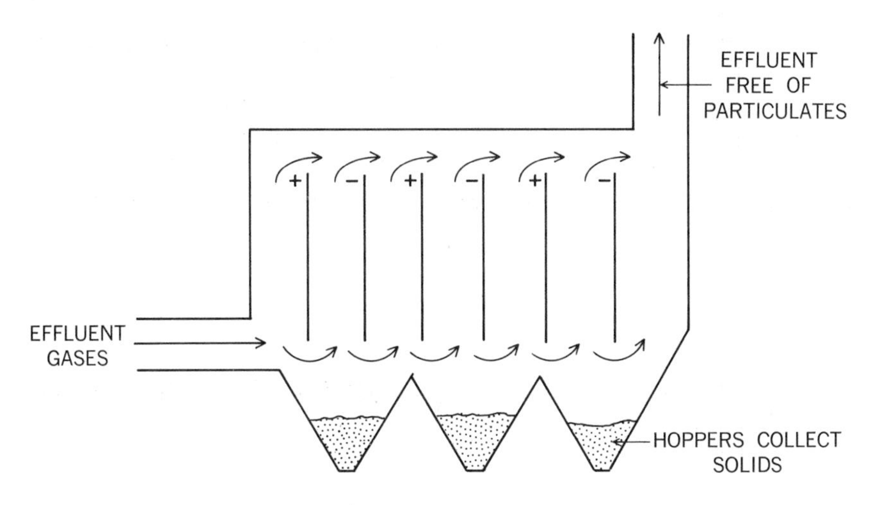

FIGURE 6-4 PLATE-TYPE ELECTROSTATIC PRECIPITATOR

removed. The amount of contact and interaction are increased by the use of spray chambers or towers where the liquid is introduced into the gas stream as a fine spray. Another approach frequently used is to allow the liquid to percolate downward through a packed bed of material while the gas stream moves upward through the packed bed and liquid in a counter-current fashion.

4. *Electrostatic Precipitators.* These devices are based on the fact that particulates moving through a region of high electrostatic potential tend to

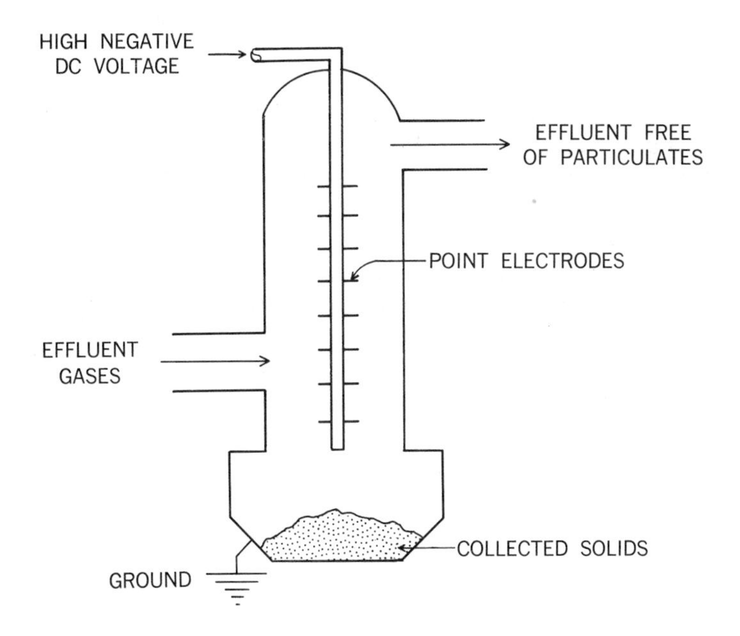

FIGURE 6-5 TUBE-TYPE ELECTROSTATIC PRECIPITATOR

become charged and are then attracted to an oppositely-charged area where they can be collected. Two basic design types, the plate and the tube, are used. The plate type consists of a series of parallel metal plates with large electric potentials that are of opposite sign on every other plate (Fig. 6-4). In the tube type, a highly charged discharge wire runs down the center of a tube, which is either grounded or highly charged with a sign opposite that of the wire. Figure 6-5 is a schematic drawing of this design.

Suggestions for Further Reading

Journal Articles

1. Bertine, K. K., and Goldberg, E. D. 1971. Fossil fuel combustion and the major sedimentary cycle. *Science* 173:233–35.
2. Lowry, W. P. 1967. The climate of cities. *Scientific American* 217: 15–23.
3. Selikoff, I. J. 1969. Asbestos. *Environment* 11 (no. 2):2–7.
4. Asbestos: friend or foe. 1970. *Environmental Science and Technology* 4:727–28.
5. Beryllium—hazardous air pollutant. 1971. *Environmental Science and Technology* 5:584–85.

Government Documents

1. U.S. Dept. of Health, Education, and Welfare. 1969. *Air quality criteria for particulate matter.* National Air Pollution Control Administration Publication No. AP–49.
2. U.S. Dept. of Health, Education, and Welfare. 1969. *Control techniques for particulate air pollutants.* National Air Pollution Control Administration Publication No. AP–51.
3. U.S. Environmental Protection Agency. 1971. *Asbestos and air pollution: an annotated bibliography.* Air Pollution Control Office Publication No. AP–82.
4. U.S. Environmental Protection Agency. 1971. *Beryllium and air pollution: an annotated bibliography.* Air Pollution Control Office Publication AP–83.

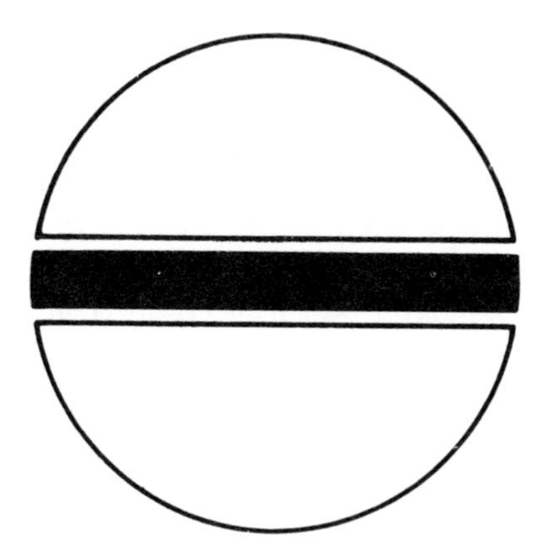

Chapter 7

Temperature Inversions and the Greenhouse Effect

While temperature inversions and the greenhouse effect are not related, as might be implied by the chapter title, both are commonly included in discussions about air pollution.

Temperature Inversions

Temperature inversions can cause serious pollution problems, not because they represent a source of pollution, but because they cause pollutants to accumulate in the lower atmosphere instead of dispersing. Many of the most serious air pollution episodes (occurrences of extremely adverse health effects) have occurred in this country during temperature inversions.

The movement of air in the atmosphere can take place vertically or horizontally. Horizontal movement is governed mainly by prevailing winds. If these winds are active and of sufficient force, pollutants have little chance to build up before they are dispersed. Surrounding mountains, hills, or even buildings in a large city slow down and break up winds and lessen the horizontal movement of air. With limited horizontal movement, pollutant dispersion becomes dependent on the vertical movement of air.

The temperature of air above the earth normally decreases with altitude. Air closest to the earth's surface is warmed by the earth, expands and becomes less dense than the cooler air above it. The warm, less dense air then rises through the cooler air, which flows in to replace it. This new lower air is then warmed, expands, and in turn rises. Air currents are created this way and pollutants are dispersed.

Occasionally this normal pattern is disrupted when a cool layer of air, from the sea for example, flows in at a low altitude and displaces the warmer air up to a higher altitude. When this occurs, the air temperature will be found to decrease from the earth's surface to some altitude (for example, 1500 or 3000 ft). This normal behavior is then replaced by an abnormal one in which the air temperature from 3000 ft to 5000 or 6000 ft increases with altitude. Beyond this layer, normal behavior again occurs as the air temperature decreases with altitude. The warm layer starting at 3000 ft and extending to 5000 or 6000 ft is the inversion layer, which effectively creates a lid for the air under it. The graphs of air temperature versus altitude given in Fig. 7-1 illustrate normal behavior and that which is characteristic of an inversion.

The presence of an inversion layer prevents vertical atmospheric circulation, since the cooler air cannot rise through the warm inversion layer. Pollutants put into the air are then trapped in the lower, noncirculating air, as illustrated in Fig. 7-2. Such situations as this may remain unchanged for days until weather conditions change and the inversion layer breaks up. An added pollution problem occurs with inversion layers in the form of increased photochemical activity. The inversion layer is usually warm, dry, and cloudless, and so transmits a maximum amount of sunlight, which interacts photochemically with the trapped pollutants to form extreme amounts of smog. Thus high levels of smog are usually associated with air pollution episodes involving temperature inversions.

The Greenhouse Effect

Carbon dioxide is not normally considered to be an air pollutant, because it is a naturally occurring component of air. Carbon dioxide is continually being cycled into and out of the atmosphere in a cycle involving the activities of plants and animals. In this carbon cycle, plants, by means of photosynthesis,

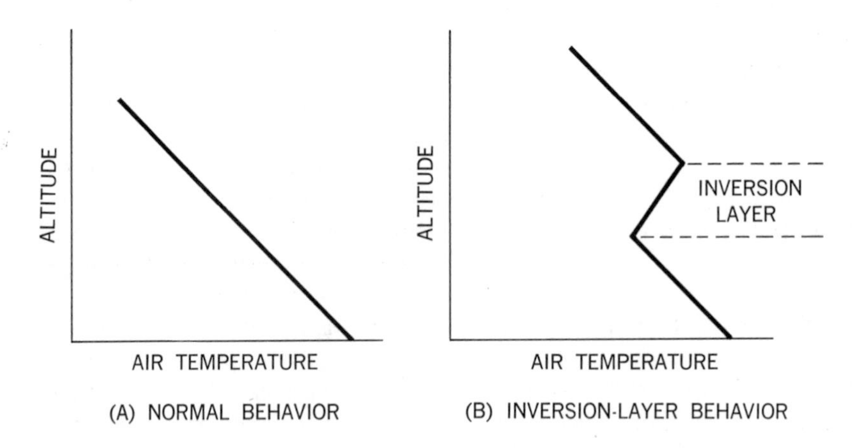

FIGURE 7-1 AIR TEMPERATURE AS A FUNCTION OF ALTITUDE

Redrawn, with modifications, from P. R. Ehrlich and A. H. Ehrlich, *Population, Resources and Environment* (San Francisco: W. H. Freeman Co., 1970), p. 124.

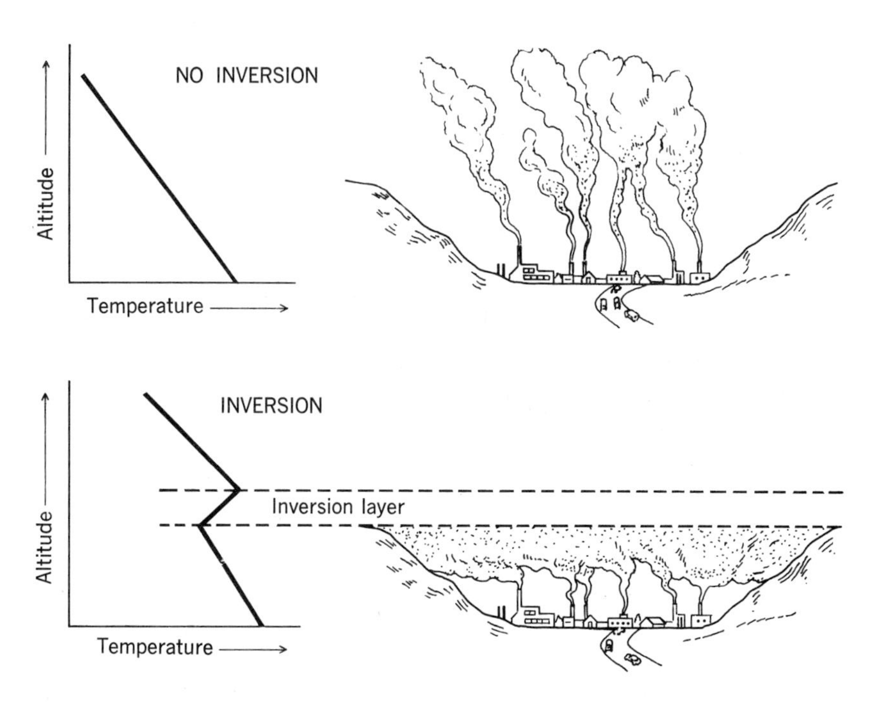

FIGURE 7-2 Temperature Inversion, in Which a Layer of Warm Air Overlies a Layer of Cooler Air, Trapping Air Pollution Close to the Ground

Redrawn from P. R. Ehrlich and A. H. Ehrlich, *Population, Resources and Environment* (San Francisco: W. H. Freeman Co., 1970), p. 124.

use light energy to react CO_2 from the air with water and produce carbohydrates and oxygen. The carbohydrates are stored in the plant, and the oxygen is released into the atmosphere. When plants are oxidized by natural decomposition, burning, or consumption by animals, oxygen is absorbed from the air and CO_2 released back into the atmosphere. In a simplified fashion, this is the carbon cycle of nature which results essentially in a constant atmospheric CO_2 level if it is not upset by man.

Man has disrupted the carbon cycle by clearing land, which decreases the available plants; by burning fossil fuels; and by converting limestone into cement. The first activity decreases nature's ability to remove atmospheric CO_2, while the latter two increase the amount in the atmosphere. The net effect is an increasing atmospheric CO_2 level. The most significant activity of the three is the burning of fossil fuels. The increasing CO_2 level in the atmosphere is shown for the last century in Fig. 7-3.

The greenhouse effect results from an interaction between the increasing amount of atmospheric CO_2 and solar radiation. Although sunlight consists of many wavelengths, much of the radiation reaching the earth's surface is in the range of visible light. This is because ozone, which exists naturally in the upper atmosphere, filters out most ultraviolet light (wavelengths shorter than visible). Atmospheric water vapor and CO_2 absorb much of the incoming in-

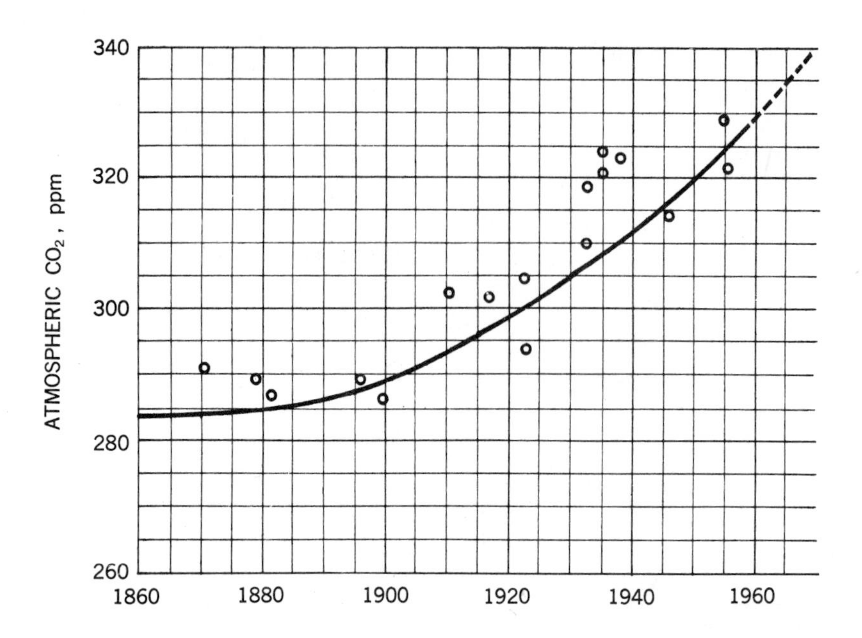

FIGURE 7-3 Rising Carbon Dioxide Concentration in the Atmosphere During the Present Century (Due to Man's Increased Burning of Fossil Fuels and Greater Agricultural Activities)

From "Carbon Dioxide and Climate" by Gilbert N. Plass. Copyright © 1959 by Scientific American, Inc. All rights reserved. Reprinted in *Man and the Ecosphere* (San Francisco: W. H. Freeman and Co., 1971), p. 175. The data on which this chart is based were compiled by G. S. Callendar.

frared light (wavelengths longer than visible) which we detect on our skin as heat.

Approximately one-third of the light that does reach the earth's surface is reflected back into space. Most of the remaining two-thirds is absorbed by such inanimate matter as rocks, concrete, and so forth. This absorbed light is re-radiated in the form of long-wavelength infrared radiation or heat when the earth cools. Light with these longer wavelengths is absorbed by atmospheric CO_2, releasing heat that raises the temperature of the atmosphere. The CO_2 is effectively behaving as a one-way filter, allowing visible light to pass through in one direction, but preventing the light in a longer wavelength form from passing in the opposite direction. This behavior is represented in Fig. 7-4 (see following page). It should be mentioned that H_2O and ozone act as filters in the same way as CO_2, but their concentrations are not being appreciably affected by man and so their contribution to the atmospheric temperature remains constant.

The one-way filter action of CO_2 leads to predictions that the temperature of the atmosphere and earth will increase. This is the origin of the term "greenhouse effect," since the temperature in greenhouses is increased by the use of glass panels which act as one-way filters. The same result can be experienced inside an automobile on a sunny day.

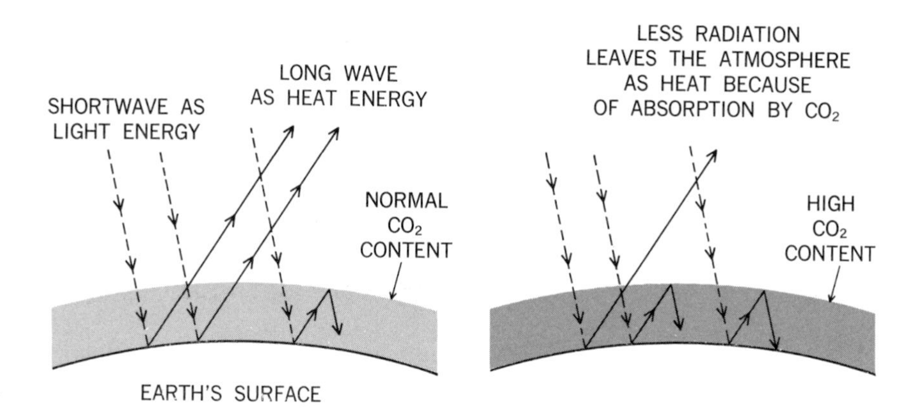

FIGURE 7-4 Shortwave Radiation (Light) Strikes the Earth and is Transformed into Longwave Radiation (Heat). Since Carbon Dioxide Absorbs Longwave Radiation, the More Carbon Dioxide Contained in the Atmosphere, the More Heat Is Retained and the Warmer the Atmosphere Becomes.

Redrawn, with permission, from Richard H. Wagner, *Environment and Man* (New York: W. W. Norton & Company, Inc., © 1971 by W. W. Norton & Company, Inc.), p. 190.

Between 1885–1940 the world-wide average temperature did increase by 0.9°F. However, from 1940–1960 a decline of 0.2°F was noted in the world-wide average, but Europe and North America experienced additional slight increases. The drop in the worldwide average is attributed to a cyclic variation in airborne particulates which reflect sunlight. The average temperature has been found to drop following major volcanic eruptions such as those of 1953 in Alaska and 1956 in Russia.

It has been predicted that a doubling of atmospheric CO_2 levels from 0.03% to 0.06% would cause a worldwide temperature increase at the earth's surface of 4.25°F. This increase would occur if other variables, such as atmospheric concentrations of particulates, remain constant. An average temperature increase of this magnitude could lead to increased melting of ice caps and glaciers. The ice caps of the earth are estimated to contain in excess of 7 million cubic miles of water, which, if all released, would increase the average depth of all oceans by 200 to 250 feet.

No melting of the ice caps has been observed yet, but some predictions are that these effects could show up in the next 30–80 years. Some melting might take place, but total conversion of the earth's ice into liquid water seems highly unlikely when the actual energy requirements are considered. For example, the energy given up when 300 liters of air is cooled 1°C (1.8°F) would melt only one gram of ice if the ice was already at the melting temperature.

Some scientists feel that rather than a flood, an ice age is more likely. Their calculations indicate that the cooling of the earth's atmosphere caused by increased particulate pollution makes an ice age a possibility for the future.

Obviously, a number of variables are involved in all of these predictions, and the net effect of atmospheric pollutants on the climate and weather remain to be seen. They could prove to be very profound, or they might even cancel one another out.

Suggestions for Further Reading

Journal Articles

1. McDermott, W. 1961. Air pollution and public health. *Scientific American* 205:49–57.
2. Peterson, E. K. 1970. The atmosphere: a clouded horizon. *Environment* 12 (no. 3):32–39.
3. Plass, G. N. 1959. Carbon dioxide and climate. *Scientific American* 201:41–47.

PART TWO

WATER POLLUTION

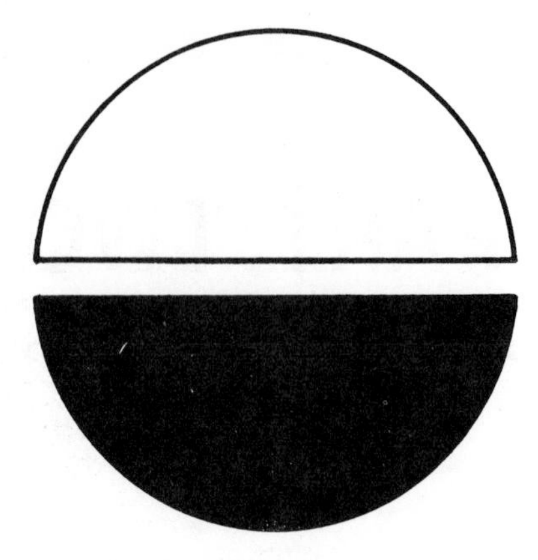

Chapter 8

Water Pollution–General Considerations

This chapter presents an overview of water pollution. Before air pollution was discussed, a comparison was made between polluted and unpolluted air. A similar comparison of polluted and unpolluted water is in order before specific water pollutants are discussed.

Unpolluted vs. Polluted Water—A Comparison

Strictly speaking, pollution is any departure from purity. When environmental pollution is the topic, the term has come to mean a departure from a normal, rather than from a pure state. This is particularly true for water. This widely distributed substance is such a good solvent that it is never found naturally in a completely pure state.

Even in the most unpolluted geographical areas, rainwater contains dissolved CO_2, O_2, and N_2 and may also carry in suspension dust or other particulates picked up from the atmosphere. Surface and well waters usually contain dissolved compounds of metals like Na, Mg, Ca, and Fe. The term *hard water* is used to describe water that contains appreciable amounts of such compounds. Even drinking water is not pure in a chemical sense. Suspended solids have been removed and harmful bacteria destroyed, but many substances still remain in solution. Indeed, absolutely pure water would not be pleasant to drink, for it is the impurities that give water the characteristic "taste" by which it is recognized.

In light of the above facts the term *pure*, when used in a water pollution context, will mean a state of water in which no substance is present in sufficient concentration to prevent the water from being used for purposes thought of as normal. Normal areas of use include:

1. Recreation and aesthetics
2. Public water supply
3. Fish, other aquatic life, and wildlife
4. Agriculture
5. Industry

Any substance that prevents the normal use of water must be considered a water pollutant. Part of the complexity of the water pollution problem arises because the normal uses of water are so varied. Water, suited for some uses and therefore considered to be unpolluted, may have to be considered to be polluted when other uses are contemplated.

Classification of Water Pollutants

The signs of water pollution are obvious to even the most casual observer. Drinking water tastes bad; masses of aquatic weeds are growing unchecked in many bodies of water; ocean beaches, rivers, and lakes emit disgusting odors; game and commercial fish are decreasing in numbers, and the meat of some of them is tainted; and oil can be seen floating on the surface of some bodies of water or deposited as scum on beaches. The diversity of these signs and effects indicates the complexity of the problem. The origins of these problems must be attributed to many sources and types of pollutants. To aid in a systematic discussion of water pollutants, they will be classified into 9 categories, given below. Each category is discussed in this chapter and then some specific pollutants are studied in more detail in the following chapters.

1. Oxygen-demanding wastes
2. Disease-causing agents
3. Plant nutrients
4. Synthetic organic compounds
5. Oil
6. Inorganic chemicals and mineral substances
7. Sediments
8. Radioactive materials
9. Heat

Some overlap between categories is unavoidable, because some wastes contain more than one pollutant. Raw sewage, for example, is an oxygen-demanding waste which may contain disease-causing agents and plant nutrients.

Oxygen-Demanding Wastes

Dissolved oxygen is a fundamental requirement of life for the plant and animal population in any given body of water. Their survival depends upon the ability of the water to maintain certain minimal concentrations of this vital substance.

Fish require the highest levels, invertebrates lower levels, and bacteria the least. For a diversified warm-water biota, including game fish, the dissolved oxygen (DO) concentrations should be at least 5 mg/ℓ (5 ppm). For a cold-water biota, DO concentrations at or near saturation values are desirable. The minimum level should be no lower than 6 ppm. The amount of DO at saturation varies with water temperature and altitude. At 20°C and 1 atmosphere of pressure, the value is 9 ppm. High mountain lakes may contain 20–40% less DO than similar lakes at sea level.

A body of water is classified as polluted when the DO concentration drops below the level necessary to sustain a normal biota for that water. The primary cause of water deoxygenation is the presence of substances collectively called *oxygen-demanding wastes*. These are substances easily broken down or decayed by bacterial activity in the presence of oxygen. The available dissolved oxygen is consumed by bacterial activity, and thus, the presence of such materials quickly leads to a depletion of dissolved oxygen.

Although some inorganic substances are found in this category, most oxygen-demanding wastes are organic compounds. Pollutants in this category typically come from such sources as sewage, both domestic and animal; industrial wastes from food processing plants; wastes from paper mill activities; tanning operation by-products; and effluent from slaughterhouses and meat-packing plants. The effects of adding these materials to water are a function of the amount of water available for dilution. For this reason, it is not surprising to find that low DO problems are especially common in late summer and early fall, when water levels are normally low.

Most compounds involved in this type of pollution contain carbon as their most abundant element. One reaction they undergo, with bacterial help, is the oxidation of carbon to CO_2.

$$C + O_2 \rightarrow CO_2 \qquad \text{(eq. 8-1)}$$

In this reaction 32 grams of oxygen are required to oxidize 12 grams of carbon. The carbon can thus be thought of as demanding nearly three times its weight in oxygen for the reaction to take place. On this basis, 9 ppm of oxygen is needed to react with approximately 3 ppm of dissolved carbon. This amounts to a reaction between the dissolved oxygen from a gallon of water and a small drop of oil. It becomes easy to see how waters can quickly be depleted of dissolved oxygen.

Because oxygen-demanding wastes rapidly deplete the DO of water, it is important to be able to estimate the amount of these pollutants in a given body of water. The biochemical oxygen demand (BOD) of water is a quantity related to the amount of wastes present. In a water sample, the BOD indicates the amount of dissolved oxygen used up during the oxidation of oxygen-demanding wastes. It is measured by incubating a sample of water for five days at 20°C. The amount of oxygen consumed (BOD) is determined by chemical determination of the DO concentration of the water before and after incubation.

A BOD of 1 ppm is characteristic of nearly pure water. Water is considered fairly pure with a BOD of 3 ppm, and of doubtful purity when the BOD value reaches 5 ppm. Public health authorities object to run-off entering streams if the BOD of the run-off exceeds 20 ppm. A comparison of these BOD levels with the range of values characteristic of the sources given in Table 8-1 indicates the seriousness of the problem. Obviously, the pollutants

TABLE 8-1 CHARACTERISTIC BOD LEVELS

SOURCE	BOD RANGE (ppm)
Untreated municipal sewage	100–400
Run-off from barnyards and feed lots	100–10,000
Food processing wastes	100–10,000

Data selected from U.S. Dept. of Agriculture, *Wastes in Relation to Agriculture and Forestry*, pp. 41–44.

of Table 8-1 must be highly diluted upon entering water if the dissolved oxygen is not to be rapidly and completely depleted. The problem is especially critical for bodies of water already low in dissolved oxygen.

An interesting way to point out the magnitude of the oxygen-demanding waste problem is to equate the BOD of the total daily nationwide wastes from specific sources to the number of humans required to produce daily waste with an equivalent BOD. Table 8-2 shows such a comparison for selected agricul-

TABLE 8-2 POPULATION EQUIVALENT FOR BOD SOURCES

SOURCE OF WASTE	POPULATION EQUIVALENT (MILLIONS)
Canneries	8.0
Cotton processing	5.1
Dairy processes	11.9
Meat slaughtering	13.7
Paper and pulp processing	216.0
Domestic animal waste	1,900.0

Data selected from U.S. Dept. of Agriculture, *Wastes in Relation to Agriculture and Forestry*, pp. 41, 46.

tural and forestery wastes. Notice the large contribution by domestic animals. On a daily basis, they produce as much oxygen-demanding waste as a population of 1.9 billion people. The trend is toward concentrating these animals into smaller and smaller areas (feed lots). This leads to very serious BOD problems in some localized areas. Table 8-3 contains a breakdown, by animal, of BOD population equivalents. This population equivalent is in terms of fecal production.

TABLE 8-3 POPULATION EQUIVALENT FOR ANIMALS

ANIMAL	HUMAN POPULATION BOD EQUIVALENT
Man	1.0
Horse	11.3
Cow	16.4
Sheep	2.5
Hog	1.9
Hen	0.1

Adapted from part of a table in U.S. Dept. of Agriculture, *Wastes in Relation to Agriculture and Forestry*, p. 41.

The disappearance of plant and animal life is an obvious result of the oxygen depletion of water. This takes place by a direct killing effect or because of migrations to other areas. A less obvious but important result is a shift in water conditions from those favoring aerobic (oxygen required) activity to those that support anaerobic (oxygen not needed) activity. This occurs when the oxygen levels become so low that the aerobic microorganisms are destroyed or driven away and anaerobic ones take their place. The products of decomposition following these different pathways are quite different, as shown in Table 8-4.

TABLE 8-4 COMPARISON OF DECOMPOSITION END PRODUCTS UNDER DIFFERING CONDITIONS

AEROBIC CONDITIONS	ANAEROBIC CONDITIONS
$C \rightarrow CO_2$	$C \rightarrow CH_4$
$N \rightarrow NH_3 + HNO_3$	$N \rightarrow NH_3$ + amines
$S \rightarrow H_2SO_4$	$S \rightarrow H_2S$
$P \rightarrow H_3PO_4$	$P \rightarrow PH_3$ and phosphorus compounds

Redrawn, with permission, from L. Klein, *River Pollution*, Vol. II: *Causes and Effects* (London: Butterworth & Co., Ltd., 1962).

Methane (CH_4) is odorless and flammable; amines have a fishy smell; hydrogen sulfide is bad smelling and toxic; and some phosphorus compounds have unpleasant odors. When these contributions are added to the odor of decaying fish or algae, it becomes apparent that a shift from aerobic to anaerobic conditions of decomposition is not one favored by users of fresh air.

Disease-Causing Agents

Water is a potential carrier of pathogenic microorganisms and can endanger health and life. The pathogens most frequently transmitted through water are those responsible for infections of the intestinal tract (typhoid and para-typhoid fevers, dysentery, and cholera) and those responsible for polio and infectious hepatitis. Historically, the prevention of water-borne diseases was the primary reason for pollution control in water. Modern disinfection techniques have greatly reduced this danger in the United States. This is not true for some large parts of the world, where, for example, cholera epidemics are still common. The decrease of the water-borne disease hazard in the United States is illustrated in Fig. 8-1, where the typhoid fever death rate is shown over a period between 1880 and 1970. The fact that such disease-causing agents are under control must not result in a sense of false security. The occurrence of a polluted water supply leading to an outbreak of disease is always a possibility. The responsible organisms are present in the feces or urine of infected people and are ultimately discharged into a water supply.

Even though it might seem desirable, a direct check for these organisms is not routinely performed on water supplies. Instead, indirect methods are

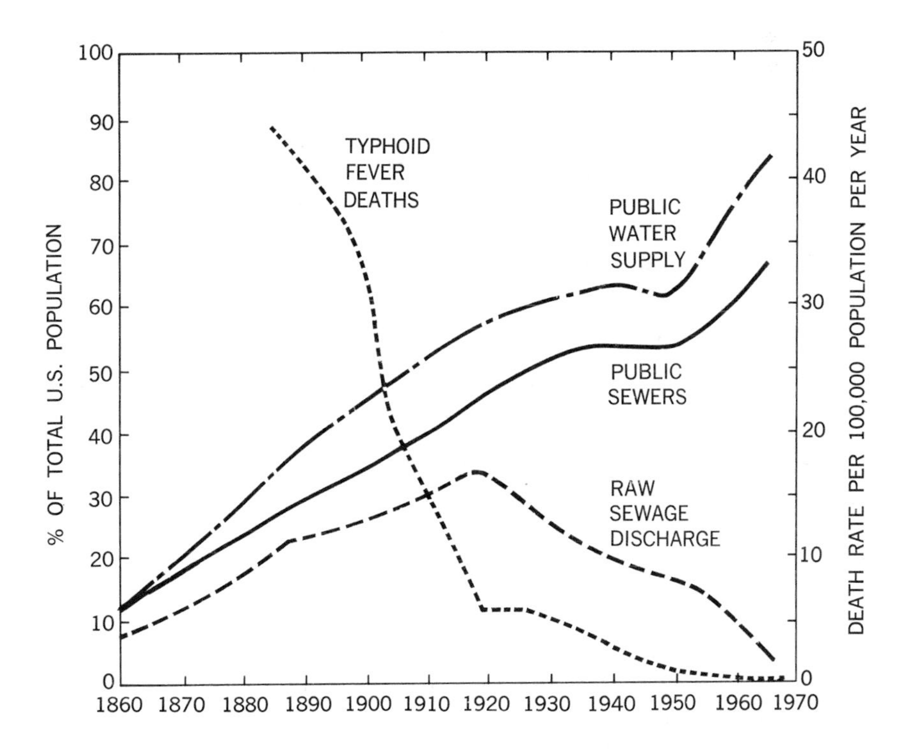

FIGURE 8-1 Growth of Public Water Supply and Sewerage in the United States (Showing the Slow but Steady Decline of Typhoid Fever Deaths During the First Sanitary Movement Beginning in 1860, Followed by the Crisis Period of World War II and the Beginning of the Second Sanitary Movement of 1950).

Redrawn from Pitts and Metcalf, *Advances in Environmental Sciences*, vol. 1 (New York: Wiley-Interscience, 1969), p. 48.

used for the following reasons. Pathogens are likely to gain entrance into water only sporadically, and once in the water they do not survive for long periods of time. Consequently, their presence could easily be missed by routine sampling. Laboratory procedures are likely to fail to detect pathogens that are present in very small numbers. Also it takes 24 hours or longer to obtain results from a laboratory examination. If pathogens were found in a water sample, it is likely that many people already would have used the water and be subject to infection.

An indicator organism, Coliform bacteria, forms the basis of the indirect method commonly used. These benign organisms live in the large intestine and absorb nutrients from their surroundings. They incite no diseases and are always present in feces. Their presence in water is an indication of fecal discharge into the water. These organisms are present in large numbers, making their detection quite easy. It is estimated that billions are excreted by an average person per day. These natural inhabitants of the human bowel do not find environmental conditions in natural waters suitable for multiplication and, in fact, they begin to die rapidly. Their presence in water samples therefore permits a rough diagnosis to be made of the time elapsed since fecal contamination took place. If fecal contamination is recent, it can be assumed that pathogenic organisms may be present along with the harmless Coliform bacteria. The absence of Coliform bacteria implies that recent intestinal discharges are not present in the water, and presumably the water is free of pathogens.

It should be mentioned that bacteria responsible for the decomposition of the organic constituents of sewage have no sanitary or public health significance. They are not found in the intestinal tracts of man or animals, and they are not pathogenic.

Plant Nutrients

Nutrients are an important limiting factor in the growth of all plants. With all other factors equal, the rate and profuseness of plant growth are proportional to the amount of nutrient available.

The enrichment of water with nutrients is a naturally occurring biological process called *eutrophication*. The term comes from two Greek words meaning "well nourished." This enrichment leads to other slow processes collectively referred to as *natural aging of lakes*. In some pollution articles, the term eutrophication includes both nutrient enrichment and lake-aging processes. The existence of peat and muck soils and deposits of coal and oil are proof that eutrophication and aging have taken place in the past. The steps in eutrophication and aging of a lake are as follows:

1. Streams from a drainage basin gradually bring soil and nutrients to a newly formed lake, increasing the fertility of the lake water.
2. The increased fertility gives rise to an accumulating growth of aquatic organisms, both plant and animal.

3. As living matter increases and organic deposits pile up on the bottom of the lake, it becomes more shallow, warmer, and richer in nutrients.
4. Plants take root at the bottom and gradually occupy more and more of the space. Their remains accelerate the filling of the basin.
5. The lake gradually becomes a marsh and finally a field or forest as it is overrun by vegetation.

The time required for this aging process to be completed is measured in thousands of years. The actual time depends upon the size and mineral content of the basin, and the climate.

In a strict sense, eutrophication is not considered to be a matter of water pollution, because it takes place naturally and some is necessary or aquatic life could not survive. It does become a pollution problem when man, through his activities, accelerates the process and the resultant aging of lakes. The high concentration of nutrients resulting when natural and man-caused contributions combine produces rapid plant growth which first becomes apparent as algae blooms. The term *bloom* is used when the concentration of individual species exceeds 500 individuals per milliliter of water.

The algae blooms and large amounts of other aquatic weeds create numerous problems. The excessive plant growth is often unsightly and interferes with recreational uses of water. The blooms also contribute unpleasant tastes and odors to water and become consumers of dissolved oxygen upon dying and decaying. This latter process leads to the deoxygenation effects previously discussed.

The growth of green plants, including algae, requires the availability of from fifteen to twenty elements which, together with their chemical symbols, are given in Table 8-5. The relative amounts of these elements required for

TABLE 8-5 ELEMENTS NECESSARY FOR PLANT GROWTH

Carbon (C)	Magnesium (Mg)	Boron (B)
Hydrogen (H)	Calcium (Ca)	Vanadium (V)
Oxygen (O)	Sodium (Na)	Chlorine (Cl)
Nitrogen (N)	Iron (Fe)	Molybdenum (Mo)
Phosphorus (P)	Manganese (Mn)	Cobalt (Co)
Sulfur (S)	Copper (Cu)	Silicon (Si)
Potassium (K)	Zinc (Zn)	

Data selected from U.S. Senate Subcommittee on Air and Water Pollution Hearings, *Water Pollution—1970*, part 2, p. 881.

plant growth depend upon the species involved. The amounts required for the growth of three typical nuisance algae are given in Table 8-6. The values are based on chemical analyses of the dried algae.

It is apparent that the major element required for growth of these algae is carbon. Nearly 0.5 lbs. is required to produce 1.0 lb. of dry Anabena algae.

TABLE 8-6 CHEMICAL COMPOSITION OF THREE NUISANCE ALGAE

ELEMENT	ALGAE		
	Microcystis	Anabena	Cladophora
C	46.5 wt%	49.7 wt%	35.3 wt%
N	8.1	9.4	2.3
P	0.7	0.77	0.56
K	0.8	1.2	6.1
Ca	0.53	0.36	1.7
S	0.27	0.53	1.6
Fe	0.27	0.08	0.23
Mg	0.17	0.42	0.23
Na	0.04	0.18	0.18
Mn	0.03	0.008	0.10
Zn	0.005	0.000	0.001
Cu	0.004	0.007	0.019
B	0.0004		0.0085

Note: Hydrogen and oxygen constitute the major unreported portion of the analyses. These elements are abundantly available at all times as water, H_2O.

Adapted from U.S. Senate Subcommittee on Air and Water Pollution Hearings, *Water Pollution—1970*, part 2, p. 882.

Nitrogen, potassium, and phosphorus follow in importance for the Microcystis and Anabena algae.

Most elements needed for plant growth are available to the plant in amounts well in excess of the plant's needs. A few, however, are present in amounts very close to the quantities required for plant growth. These may be utilized by the plant almost to the point of exhaustion. Considerable interest is centered around these elements because they appear to behave as natural controls in preventing excessive plant growth. The growth of a plant will cease when the least available element has been depleted. Man's role in eutrophication appears to be one of increasing the amounts of these growth-limiting elements. Great changes in the availability of some elements in water have occurred through man's activities.

Many studies are in progress in which relationships are being sought between concentrations of nutrients present in water and the needs of plants. Such research into the water chemistry of nutrient cycles has turned out to be a very complex problem because of the variability of aquatic systems. Typical problem areas are:

1. Chemical analyses of algae have not resulted in a definition of the limiting amounts of nutrients required to support their growth. Partly this is because of the unique ability of algae to absorb large excesses of an element. This phenomenon is called "luxury" uptake or consumption and occurs very rapidly when plentiful supplies of nutrients reach a growing body of

algae. The excess element absorbed during this process is readily released by the cells to supply growth needs at later times.

2. Different species of algae have different minimum requirements for elements.
3. Different bodies of water have different basic ratios of nutrients which depend on the geological surroundings of the water.
4. Many sources of nutrients are available and all must be taken into consideration. Some nutrients may be taken from the air and used directly. This means that factors other than aqueous nutrient concentrations must be considered.

Results so far indicate that one key limiting reactant will not be found. The three elements studied in greatest detail, phosphorus, nitrogen, and carbon have all been found to be limiting reactants depending upon water conditions. Phosphorus may be limiting to algal growth in nutrient-poor lakes, but it may be present in excess in nutrient-rich lakes. It is generally agreed that nitrogen is a limiting nutrient in some lakes and in many or perhaps most estuarine and coastal waters. Carbon appears to be a limiting factor only under restricted circumstances such as those present in extremely eutrophic soft-water lakes.

Both nitrogen and phosphorus are present in small amounts in natural waters, but their concentrations have been greatly increased by the activities of man. As much as 80% of the nitrogen and 75% of the phosphorus added to surface waters in the U.S. originate from man-made sources. Table 8-7 gives estimates of possible nutrient discharge (as P and N) into estuaries from a hypothetical community. The community is made up of 10 million people and the nutrients are put into a river discharging 15,000 cubic feet of water per second into the estuaries. It is assumed that 20 volumes of seawater dilute each volume of discharged river water.

TABLE 8-7 EXAMPLE OF POSSIBLE NUTRIENT DISCHARGES TO ESTUARIES FROM VARIOUS SOURCES (METRIC TONS PER YEAR)

	NITROGEN (N)	PHOSPHORUS (P)
Sewage: population of 10 million, per capita generation 400 liters/day	6,000	15,000
River water: discharge 500 m^3/sec (approx. 15,000 cfs)	300	7
Subsurface seawater: 20 volumes of seawater mixing with each volume of river water	6,000	900
Storm-water runoff: 75 cm (30 inches) per year area	6,000	800

Redrawn from *Man's Impact on the Global Environment*, p. 148 (Report of the Study of Critical Environmental Problems [Cambridge, Mass.: The MIT Press, 1970]).

The dominant source of phosphorus is seen to be sewage, while nitrogen in various forms is supplied in nearly equal amounts by sewage treatment plants, storm-water runoff, and subsurface seawater.

The phosphorus content of domestic sewage has become a topic of concern. It has been estimated that up to 70% of this comes from the use of household detergents, and it should be subject to rather easy control procedures. The elimination of phosphorus compounds from detergents has been discussed at great length: these detergents and their contributions to water pollution constitute the topics of Chapter 11.

Synthetic Organic Compounds

The production of synthetic organic chemicals in the U.S. has increased by a factor of nearly 14 since the end of World War II. This is illustrated by Table 8-8. Compounds included in this group are used as fuels, plastics, plasticizers, fibers, elastomers, solvents, detergents, paints, insecticides, food additives, and pharmaceuticals. Of these, two (detergents and insecticides), have been the subjects of intensive study. They are the subjects of Chapters 11 and 12, respectively.

TABLE 8-8 SYNTHETIC ORGANIC COMPOUND PRODUCTION

YEAR	PRODUCTION (BILLIONS OF LBS.)
1943	10
1953	24
1963	61
1967	102
1968	114
1969	126
1970	138

Data compiled from *Chemical and Engineering News* 47:77A (September 1, 1969), and J. N. Pitts and R. L. Metcalf, eds., *Advances in Environmental Science*, Vol. 1, p. 7 (New York: Wiley-Interscience, 1969).

Much more work is needed to determine the relationships to the environment of many of these other types of compounds. The following facts are known about them:

1. Some are resistant to biochemical breakdown by natural water bacteria or waste treatment processes and therefore persist for extended periods of time in water.
2. Some are responsible for objectionable and offensive tastes, odors, and colors of some fish and shellfish taken from polluted water.

3. Some are toxic to fish and other aquatic life when present in very low concentrations.

Since the use of these compounds is expanding so rapidly, it is important that certain facts be determined. The distribution, fate, and potentially hazardous effects should be the topics of future research.

Oil

In 1859 the first successful oil well in the U.S. was brought into production at Titusville, Pennsylvania. The infant oil industry produced about 2000 barrels of crude oil that year. Annual crude oil production in the U.S. is now over 3 billion barrels.

The production, distribution, and use of such large yearly quantities results in some oil contamination of the environment. Some of this contamination is accidental, some is not. Chapter 13 is devoted to a discussion of the problem of oil pollution.

Inorganic Chemicals and Mineral Substances

This category of water pollutants includes inorganic salts, mineral acids, and finely divided metals or metal compounds. These substances enter natural waters as a result of activities in various smelting, metallurgical, and chemical industries; mine drainage; and various natural processes. The presence of these pollutants in water results in three general effects: the acidity, salinity, and toxicity of the water may be increased.

Acid mine drainage is the primary source of pollutants that increase water acidity. This drainage adversely affects thousands of miles of streams and is one of the most significant causes of water quality degradation in coal-producing areas. The actual pollutants present in mine drainage are sulfuric acid (H_2SO_4) and soluble compounds of iron. These substances are formed as the result of a reaction between air, water, and pyrite (FeS_2) present in coal seams. Certain types of bacteria are involved in the reaction, but their role is not completely understood. This reaction can take place in both underground and surface mines.

During mining operations in deep mines, the strata between the coal seam and the surface are invariably disturbed. Fissures appear through which water drains into the mine from many surface areas. This water containing the harmful pollutants is eventually discharged into surface streams, either naturally or through man-made processes. Damaging mine drainage is formed in surface mines if the surface run-off water comes in contact with pyrite-containing coal.

The total unneutralized acid drainage from coal mines in the U.S. is estimated at more than 4 million tons of H_2SO_4 equivalent per year. About 60%

of the mine drainage pollution problems originate in mines once worked but now abandoned.

At the present time, much effort is directed toward either preventing the formation of acid mine drainage or removing the pollutants by chemical treatment prior to releasing the discharge into natural waters. Three methods commonly used are:

1. *Sealing of abandoned mines.* Sealing abandoned mines to prevent the entry of air or water helps to prevent the fundamental reactions involved in acid mine drainage formation by eliminating at least one of the required reactants. The inability to attain tight seals has been a problem with this method.
2. *Drainage control.* Attempts have been made to minimize the contact time between water and pyrite by quickly removing water from mines. It has been found difficult to gather the water from the many sources available to an underground mine. This problem has curtailed some of the effectiveness of this method.
3. *Chemical treatment.* This method is being used in many active mines. The mine discharge is sent to a nearby treatment plant where hydrated lime is added. This is followed by an aeration of the water. The water is then placed in large lagoons where the sludge, created by the process, settles to the bottom, and a clear overflow is discharged into the natural waters. This process is quite simple, but problems are created by the large amounts of iron-containing sludge that are formed. These materials present disposal problems. Also, the use of lime generally leaves the water saturated with dissolved salts.

There is still a great deal of research needed if the problems of acid mine drainage are to be solved.

Coal mining is not the only source of acidic water pollutants. Other types of mining make their contributions, as do various other industries. Large amounts of acid are used to clean oxides and grease from metals. The used acids from these pickling operations become serious problems in some localized areas.

Because of the presence in solution of carbonate ($CO_3^{=}$) and bicarbonate (HCO_3^-) ions, the *p*H of most productive, fresh natural waters is between 6.5 and 8.5. This natural buffer system makes it possible for small amounts of acid or base to dissolve in the waters without causing appreciable changes in the *p*H. These ions also represent an indispensable reservoir for carbon needed by aquatic plants during photosynthesis. Such use of these ions by plants can affect the buffering capacity of water, since there is a decided limit on the rate at which CO_2 (the source of $CO_3^{=}$ and HCO_3^-) can be obtained from the atmosphere to replace that used by plants.

Large influxes of strong acid are able to overwhelm this buffering ability of water and cause drastic drops in *p*H values. The effects of these changes depend upon the magnitude of the *p*H drop involved. Some effects are:

1. *Aquatic life destruction.* At *p*H levels below 4.0, all vertebrates, most invertebrates, and many microorganisms are destroyed. Most higher plants are eliminated, leaving only a few algae and bacteria. Acid mine drainage is one of the primary causes of fish kills in the U.S., accounting for over one million dead fish in 1967. Excessive precipitation increases the mine drainage output and compounds the problem. During high water seasons (winter and spring), the *p*H of the waters in some areas has been found to be as low as 2.5.
2. *Corrosion.* Water with a *p*H lower than 6.0 can cause excessive corrosion of plumbing systems, boats, piers, and related structures.
3. *Agricultural crop damage.* Acidity and alkalinity of irrigation water are usually of little consequence over a *p*H range of 4.5–9.0, since the soil is a buffered system. Problems may occur if the *p*H drops below 4.5. Such acidic water increases the solubility of such substances as Fe, Al, and Mg salts. These ions, at the resulting high concentrations, are sometimes toxic to plants.

One mechanism by which fish and other aquatic animals are destroyed by acid pollution involves the equilibrium between CO_2, HCO_3^- and $CO_3^=$. At low *p*H, HCO_3^- and $CO_3^=$ are both converted to CO_2 which dissolves in water. This excessive "free" CO_2 in the water interferes with the processes by which CO_2 is eliminated from the animals.

As a result of metabolic activity, CO_2 is produced in the animal cells and moves by way of the blood to organs (gills) where it leaves the blood and diffuses into the water. An increase in external CO_2 slows the diffusion rate from the blood. The result is an accumulation of CO_2 in the blood of the animal, with the result that less oxygen can be carried by the blood and the *p*H of the blood goes down. These conditions can eventually lead to the death of the animal.

Salinity of water is not an uncommon observation. About 97% of the total water in the world is found in oceans and seas in the form of salt water. It is common knowledge that such water is not suitable for consumption by man. The remaining 3% is classified as fresh water, but it can and does acquire salinity. The sources of salinity are varied and include:

1. *Industrial Effluents.* Inorganic salts are a major constituent of many industrial effluents. Salts are the products of acid-base neutralizations, many of which are used in various smelting, metallurgical, and chemical industries. Acid mine drainage can also cause salts to be formed.
2. *Irrigation.* Water used in irrigation dissolves large amounts of minerals as it percolates down through soil.
3. *Salt Brines.* Occasionally, salt brines from mines or oil wells are released into normally fresh water.
4. *Ocean Salt.* Large rivers normally prevent salt water of the ocean from backing up by their continuous outflow. During times of low run-off, river currents may be overcome by tidal flow from the sea with the result that salty water may move many miles upstream. In 1965, for example,

the water supply of Philadelphia was threatened when the slow current of the Delaware River allowed sea water to advance almost to the city's water supply intake pipes. The problem affected other cities as well. New York City had a pressing need for water at this same time, but was forced by interstate watershed compacts to release some badly needed water from reservoirs into the Delaware to maintain a minimum flow and protect Philadelphia's supply.

5. *Highway Use.* The use of salt on highways to melt winter ice and snow is creating serious problems in rural areas of numerous states. Salt from the highways has killed nearby trees and shrubberies of frontage homesteads. Worse still, the salt has penetrated into the ground waters and polluted rural wells.

Large amounts of salinity in water cause problems other than those related to human consumption. Dissolved inorganic and mineral substances exert adverse effects on aquatic animal and plant life and cause many irrigation problems in the agricultural industry. Damage to aquatic life is primarily related to the osmosis process, assuming the dissolved substances are nontoxic. Generally, the concentration of dissolved materials in body fluids is the maximum that an aquatic organism can tolerate. When these organisms are in contact with water containing higher concentrations, there is a tendency for water to move out of the cells of the organism into the surrounding water. The resulting increase in concentration within the cells of the organism can lead to death. Many fresh water species disappear when waters become brackish.

One of the most serious long-term effects of increased salinity of waters involves the use and re-use of water in irrigation. It has been estimated that about 25% of the irrigated land of the U.S. is now affected to some degree by water salinity. Irrigation water brought onto a field always contains some dissolved salts. The concentration of these salts is in the range of 25–8000 mg/ℓ. Plants extract water from the irrigated field, but most of the dissolved salts are excluded by the roots. Water that evaporates from the soil surface leaves dissolved salts behind. These two processes cause residual salts to accumulate in the soil.

In order to preserve the salt balance of the soil and avoid damage to crops, the excess salt accumulation must be leached from the soil with excess irrigation water. Thus, drainage water from the soil contains an increased concentration of salts which it carries back to the general water supply. Irrigation does not actually produce a pollutant in the form of dissolved salts but merely returns the salts to the general water supply in a more concentrated form.

To illustrate the serious nature of this problem, assume that 20% of the total water flow in a river is withdrawn, used for irrigation, and returned at each of four successive projects along the river. The relative concentration of dissolved salts in the river will increase from an initial value of 1.00 to 1.25, 1.67, 2.50, and 5.00 following each usage.

Table 8-9 gives general crop responses to various concentrations of total dissolved inorganic solids (TDS) in irrigation water. In order to put these

TABLE 8-9 SUGGESTED GUIDELINES FOR SALINITY IN IRRIGATION WATER

CROP RESPONSE	TDS mg/ℓ	EC[1] mmhos/cm
Water for which no detrimental effects will usually be noticed	<500	<0.75
Water which can have detrimental effects on sensitive crops	500–1,000	0.75–1.50
Water that may have adverse effects on many crops and requiring careful management practices	1,000–2,000	1.50–3.00
Water that can be used for salt-tolerant plants on permeable soils with careful management practices	2,000–5,000	3.00–7.50

[1]Electrical conductivity.

Adapted from U.S. Dept. of the Interior, *Report of the Committee on Water Quality Control Administration*, p. 117.

figures into perspective, it is worth noting that the Colorado River has a TDS of 750 mg/ℓ by the time it reaches the Imperial Dam in California. Also, the recommended TDS level for drinking water is less than 200 mg/ℓ, and the permissible maximum is 500 mg/ℓ. A farmer who applies 5 feet of water during the growing season in the Imperial Valley in California also applies 6 tons of dissolved salts per acre. All crops exhibit decreased growth and yield with increasing water salinity. This is illustrated in Fig. 8-2 (see following page) for various common vegetable crops. The salinity is expressed in terms of electrical conductivity (EC) of a saturated extract of the soil. The EC values can be related to actual concentrations by use of Table 8-9.

In addition to total salt content, the nature of the individual salt components exerts effects on the soil. These components can be altered by previous use of the water. For example, water used in municipal and some industrial applications is softened before use. The ions Ca^{++} and Mg^{++} are replaced by Na^{+} resulting in water enriched with Na^{+} ions. This high Na^{+} concentration adversely affects soils and plants by breaking up soil aggregates and causing the soil to become highly impermeable.

The toxic properties of numerous inorganic compounds, particularly those of some of the heavier metallic elements, have been known for years. Some of these compounds have desirable properties and so are routinely manufactured. Appropriate precautions are taken to insure the safety of individuals involved in the manufacturing process. The use of these compounds has led to their introduction into the environment either directly or indirectly, intentionally or unintentionally. The recent detection of these metallic substances in air and water in concentrations approaching toxic levels has created a great amount of concern. The most toxic, persistent, and abundant of these compounds in the environment appear to be those of the metals mercury,

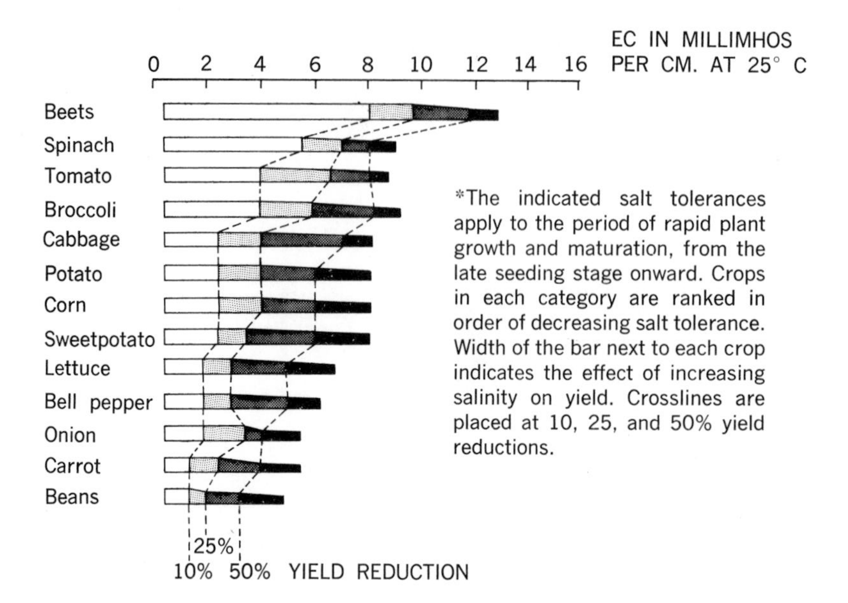

FIGURE 8-2 SALT TOLERANCE OF VEGETABLE CROPS*

Redrawn from U.S. Dept. of the Interior, *Report of the Committee on Water Quality Control Administration*, p. 117.

(Hg), lead (Pb), arsenic (As), cadmium (Cd), chromium (Cr), and nickel (Ni). These metals are known to accumulate in the bodies of organisms, remain for long periods of time, and behave as cumulative poisons. More research is needed to determine the seriousness of these potential hazards. Two representative elements of the group, mercury and lead, are the topics of Chapters 9 and 10, respectively.

Sediments

Sediments are almost taken for granted as a type of pollution because of the naturally occurring process of erosion. Sediments produced by that process do represent the most extensive pollutants of surface waters. It is estimated that suspended solid loadings reaching natural waters are at least 700 times as large as the solid loadings from sewage discharge.

Two facts not commonly known are the effects man has had on erosion rates and the far-reaching effects of sedimentation. Erosion rates of land are increased 4–9 times by agricultural development and may be increased by a factor of 100 as a result of construction activities. Strip mining activities greatly influence the rate of erosion in an area. Sediment yields from strip-mined areas average nearly 30,000 tons per square mile annually, an amount 10–60 times as great as yields from agricultural lands. The amount of sediment washed from an area depends very much upon the condition of the land. This is indicated by the data of Table 8-10. These data are based on 2.4 inches of rain in 1 hour.

TABLE 8-10 EFFECT OF GROUND COVER ON EROSION

	GOOD GROUND COVER	FAIR GROUND COVER	POOR GROUND COVER
% of ground covered with plants and litter	60–75	37	10
% of rain that runs off	2	14	73
Soil loss (tons/acre)	0.05	0.5	5.55

Data selected from U.S. Dept. of Agriculture, *Mountain Water*, p. 37.

Sediment production is a greater problem in some parts of the U.S. than in others. This variation is not all caused by man's activities, but also involves the type of soils, geology, topography, precipitation, and vegetation cover. As can be seen in Fig. 8-3, the Southwest and Midwest have the greatest sedimentation problems.

The detrimental effects of sediment in water are:

1. *Stream channels, harbors, and reservoirs are filled.* This causes channels to overflow more easily, alters flow rates and depths of channels, and

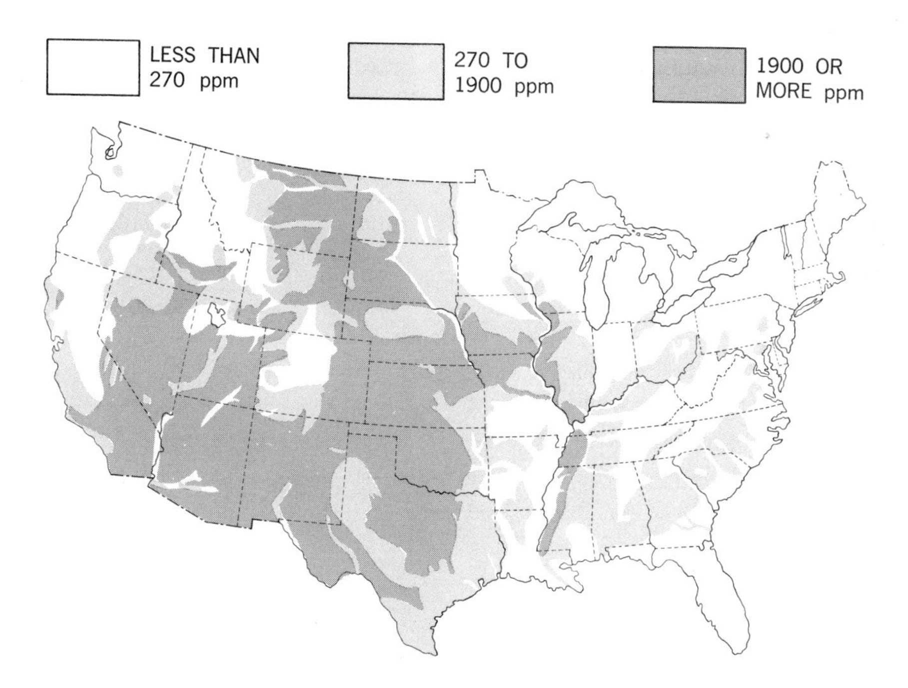

FIGURE 8-3 CONCENTRATION OF SEDIMENT IN STREAMS

Redrawn from U.S. Dept. of the Interior, *Clean Water for the 1970's*, p. 11.

reduces the useful life of reservoirs. Expensive dredging is required to counteract these effects.

2. *Destroys aquatic animals.* Sediment settling on the bottom reduces fish and shellfish populations by blanketing fish nests and food supplies.
3. *Reduces light penetration into water.* The reduction in the amount of sunlight penetrating into the water reduces the rate of photosynthesis by plants, which in turn results in a decreased production of oxygen needed for normal stream balance.
4. *Water is clouded.* This increases the cost of treating water used for culinary purposes. Sediment passing through power plant turbines causes serious abrasion and wear. The hunting ability of fish is curtailed if they depend on their vision.

Radioactive Materials

Uranium and its decay products are examples of elements which possess highly unstable nuclei. The disintegration of these nuclei results in radioactive emissions which may be highly injurious, even lethal, to living organisms. Four activities are potential sources of radioactive pollutants, and each is known to have been involved in environmental pollution.

1. The mining and processing of ores to produce usable radioactive substances.
2. The use of radioactive materials in nuclear weapons.
3. The use of radioactive materials in nuclear power plants.
4. The use of radioactive materials in medical, industrial, and research applications.

Typically, uranium ore contains about 2–5 lbs. of U_2O_3 per ton. Obviously, large amounts of ore must be processed to produce the usable material. The ore is crushed, finely ground, and leached with acid or alkali. The uranium is recovered in a usable form from the leach liquors by various precipitation, solvent extraction, or ion exchange procedures. Radioactive wastes are produced in each of these operations. Perhaps the greatest problem of radioactive pollution, as a result of uranium production, is caused by the large quantities of "uranium tailings" produced. This finely-divided solid material remains after useful materials have been leached out. Huge piles of these tailings are found in uranium producing areas. An estimated 12 million tons are piled up in the Colorado River Basin, an active center of uranium production. As is the case with the strip-mine spoil bank, no one seems interested in the tailings once mining operations are halted.

A radiation pollution problem is created by these tailings because they contain radioactive decay products of uranium. Two of these radioactive materials are thorium-230 ($^{230}_{90}Th$) and radium-226 ($^{226}_{88}Ra$). Substances such as these can be dissolved or eroded from piles of tailings by rainfall, and in this form they can find their way into the general water supply. Radium and thorium chemically resemble calcium and so tend to be absorbed by the bones when taken into the body. Some waters in the Colorado River Basin have had the concentration of $^{226}_{88}Ra$ raised to twice the maximum level permissible for human consumption.

A program of grading tailing piles and planting vegetation to reduce erosion has been followed to some extent. This method does reduce the amount of tailing radiation in surface waters.

A well-known source of radioisotopes is nuclear weapons testing. The quantity and variety of radioactive materials produced depends on the type of weapon tested. Some of the radioisotopes are very short-lived, lasting only a few seconds or minutes, while others may have a half-life of several hundred years. These materials reach the earth as radioactive fallout. Before the first test explosions were conducted, it was assumed that fallout (dust and debris) would fall to earth rather quickly and at no great distance from the detonation site, and that the spread of radioactivity would therefore be limited. It is now well-known that these assumptions were wrong, especially in the case of large explosions. Radioactive particles can, in fact, remain suspended in the air long enough to circle the globe several times, dispersing as they go. It is true, however, that the main effects of atmospheric testing are found in the immediate vicinity of the detonation site. Concern about such fallout led to the signing, in 1963, of the Limited Nuclear Test Ban Treaty. According to the terms of the treaty, the U.S. and U.S.S.R. will limit testing of nuclear weapons to underground detonations.

Underground detonations, performed in the U.S. at the Nevada test site, are designed to limit the amount of atmospheric fallout, and in most cases this is accomplished. Occasionally accidental releases of radiation reach the atmosphere because of "venting" at the explosion site. When this happens, radioactive gases are forced up through the hole used to place the explosives. The leakage may occur through channels left for control and monitoring cables, natural cracks or fissures in the rock, fractures created by the blast, or combinations of these. Sometimes venting takes place when the materials used to fill the hole are simply blown out. Leakage may occur immediately after the explosion or later, when rock and earth fall into the cavity created by the explosion and leave a channel for gas venting.

Ventings were reported in 12 of 190 tests conducted at the Nevada site from 1961 through 1969. Others are known to have occurred since 1969. The amount of radiation released is, of course, variable. It is released near ground level and thus poses no world-wide fallout problems, but it may create very serious local hazards.

Atmospheric fallout, regardless of the source, can have far-reaching effects and can be conveyed to man in a variety of ways as shown in Fig. 8-4.

Two examples of the effects of radioisotopes on man will serve to illustrate the serious nature of radioactive pollutants. Strontium-90 ($^{90}_{38}Sr$), a component of radioactive fallout, has a half-life of 28 years. Chemically, it is similar to calcium. Calcium is absorbed from the soil by plants and passed on to feeding animals, where it is used in the formation of bones and teeth.

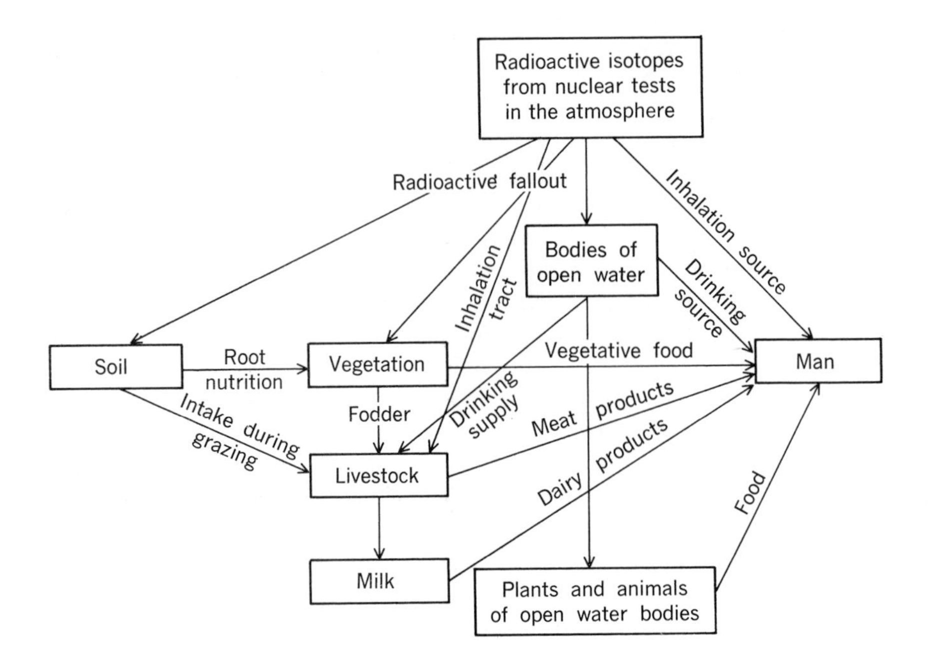

FIGURE 8-4 TRANSMISSION OF RADIOACTIVE FALLOUT TO MAN

Redrawn from U.S. Dept. of Agriculture, *Wastes in Relation to Agriculture and Forestry*, p. 18.

Man obtains calcium from both plant and animal sources such as milk, vegetables, and cereal grains. Strontium is obtained from these same sources and, because of chemical similarities to calcium, is also deposited in bones and teeth. The marrow of bones is the main site of blood-cell formation. The presence of radioactive strontium-90 in the surrounding bone tissue causes this production to be seriously curtailed. Anemia or more serious disorders may result.

Cesium-137 ($^{137}_{55}Cs$) is chemically similar to potassium, a common constituent of all living cells. Cesium from fallout is passed to man through contaminated meat and dairy products or contaminated grains and leafy vegetables. Cesium contamination of these foods results in the same effects as strontium contamination. The soft parts of the body, particularly the muscles, are adversely affected by the presence of cesium.

More and more, man is turning to nuclear generation in his attempts to satisfy an ever increasing demand for electrical power. Nuclear generators have some advantages over more commonly used types. In very large generating facilities, nuclear energy is cheaper to use than that from conventional sources like fossil fuels or falling water. Also, nuclear generators do not produce any SO_x or particulate pollutants commonly associated with fossil-fuel burning generators. By the year 2000, nuclear power is expected to be the main source of electric power generation. The statistics of Table 8-11 illustrate this fact. The units of electric energy are 10^{12} kilowatt hours.

TABLE 8-11 SOURCES OF ELECTRICAL ENERGY GENERATION

YEAR	SOURCE OF ELECTRICAL ENERGY Coal	Gas	Petroleum	Hydro	Nuclear	Total
1968	2.1	1.0	0.4	0.7	0.04	4.24
2000 (est.)	7.3	1.2	0.3	1.5	11.4	21.7

Data adapted from *Environmental Science and Technology* 5:31 (1971).

The location of existing and future nuclear power plants for electrical power generation from 1965–2020 are shown in Fig. 8-5. Nuclear power plants differ somewhat from conventional electricity generating facilities. In the conventionally fueled power plant, fossil fuel is burned to produce heat (a chemical reaction), while in a nuclear plant the heat is generated by a nuclear reaction. In each case the heat produces steam that turns a generator and produces electricity.

In a typical nuclear reactor the fuel is a mixture of uranium-235 ($^{235}_{92}U$) and uranium-238 ($^{238}_{92}U$). These isotopes are packed into stainless steel or zirconium tubes in the form of uranium oxide pellets. The total fuel load of a reactor core may contain a hundred tons or more of uranium oxide. The fuel-containing tubes are spaced in such a way as to sustain a controlled nuclear

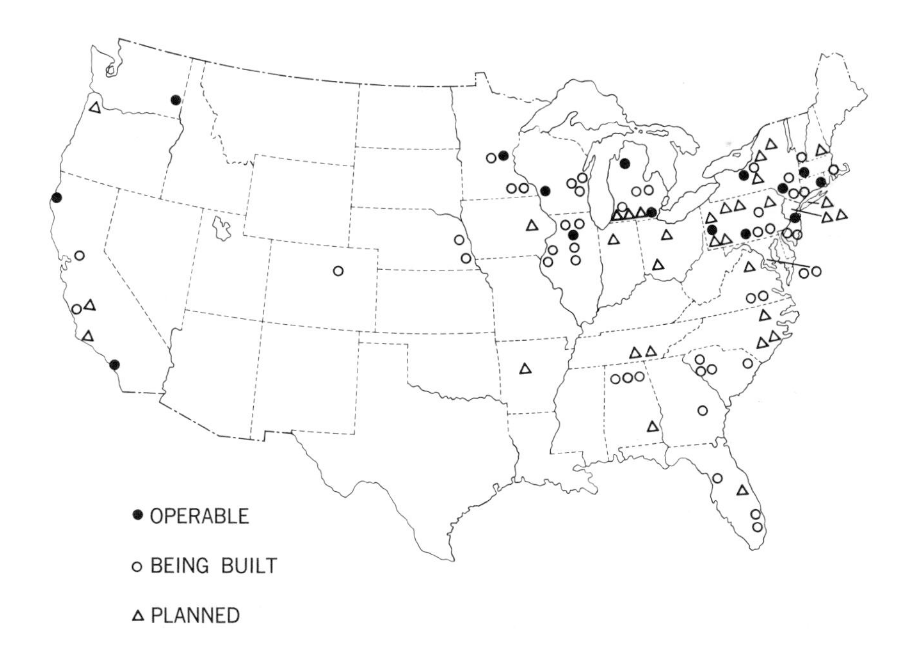

FIGURE 8-5 LOCATION OF NUCLEAR POWER PLANTS

Redrawn from U.S. Dept. of the Interior, *Clean Water for the 1970's*, p. 7.

chain reaction of the uranium atoms. This reaction generates large amounts of heat energy. The temperature of this reacting core is kept at about 1000°F by a system of circulating coolant.

In the simplest arrangement the coolant is water, which, by circulating among the fuel elements, becomes heated to boiling. The resulting steam is used to turn the turbine of an electrical generator. After passing through the turbine, this steam is condensed and cooled by a secondary cooling system, usually made up of water from a nearby river or lake. The much cooler water is then sent to the reactor core and the cycle begins again. This operation is represented in Fig. 8-6.

In less simple systems, a liquid metal (often sodium) is circulated through the reactor core, then to a heat exchanger where water is heated. The resulting steam drives a generator and the liquid metal recirculates. This type of arrangement adds the necessity of a heat exchange system between the reactor and generator turbine.

Four types of pollutants are formed by nuclear generating plants.

1. *Low level radioactive liquid wastes.* Radioactive isotopes are formed when impurities in the primary coolant water and corrosion products from

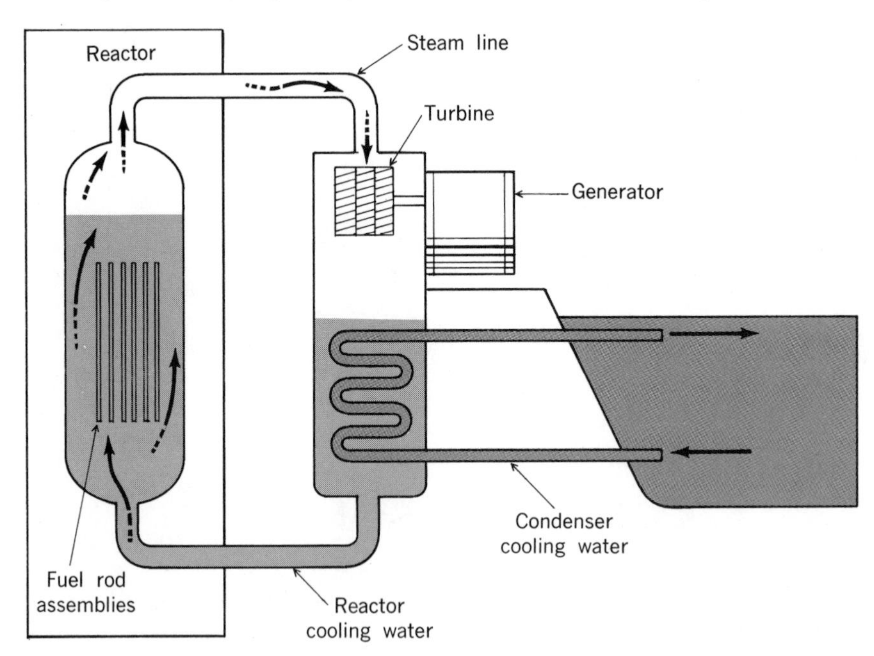

FIGURE 8-6 The Fuel Elements in a Nuclear Reactor are Usually Cooled by a Primary Coolant in a Closed System. To Cool the Primary Coolant a Secondary Coolant Is Necessary. It Is The Dumping of This Secondary Coolant into the Environment That Causes Thermal Loading Problems.

Redrawn from Richard H. Wagner, *Environment and Man* (New York: W. W. Norton & Company, Inc., 1971), p. 212, modified from *Environment* II (1969).

coolant pipes are bombarded with neutrons from the core area. This can be controlled to some degree by the use of demineralized coolant water. Much of this type of waste is now disposed of by sealing it in containers which are subsequently dropped into the ocean. There are unknowns in this disposal technique, such as the lifetime of the containers used, the waste within them, and the directions and speeds with which the containers or their contents move when subjected to underwater currents.

2. *Liquid and gaseous wastes from fuel elements.* Complete sealing of the fuel in steel or zirconium containers is apparently impossible to attain or sustain. Minute cracks allow fission products to escape into the primary coolant. This adds to the disposal problem of low level wastes discussed above.
3. *Fission products.* In 1–3 years, fission products (the ashes of nuclear fuels) accumulate to the point that they absorb sufficient neutrons to slow or stop the chain reaction. At this point, the extremely radioactive fuel elements are removed and shipped in special containers to a fuel reprocessing plant. Here the fission products are separated from the remaining usable fuel. The fuel is returned to the reactor for further use and the waste fission products are stored, in liquid form, in huge underground stainless steel tanks. Hundreds of millions of gallons of these high level wastes are now in storage.
4. *Heat.* The secondary cooling system carries huge amounts of heat away from the reactors and puts it into natural water supplies. The effect of this will be discussed as the last topic of this chapter.

A variety of research laboratories, including medical and biochemical facilities, release radioactive wastes into the air and sewer systems. It is not now feasible to attempt to collect and dispose of these materials. Nor is it feasible to collect and bury the large quantities of radioisotope-containing liquids, solids, and gases produced by laboratory uses other than research, such as diagnostics or treatment. At the present time, the amounts of radioactive waste discharged from such laboratory sources are not a threat to natural communities of plants, animals, and man.

Heat

Heat is not ordinarily thought of as a pollutant by many people, at least not in the same sense as a corrosive chemical. However, the addition of excess heat to a body of water causes adverse effects as numerous as many of the chemical pollutants. This serious problem of thermal pollution originates primarily with the practice of using water as a coolant in many industrial processes. Most water used for this purpose is returned, with the added heat, to the original sources. At present, about 70% of the water diverted to industrial use serves as a cooling medium. It is estimated that by 1980 approximately 20% of all fresh-water run-off in the U.S. will be used for cooling purposes.

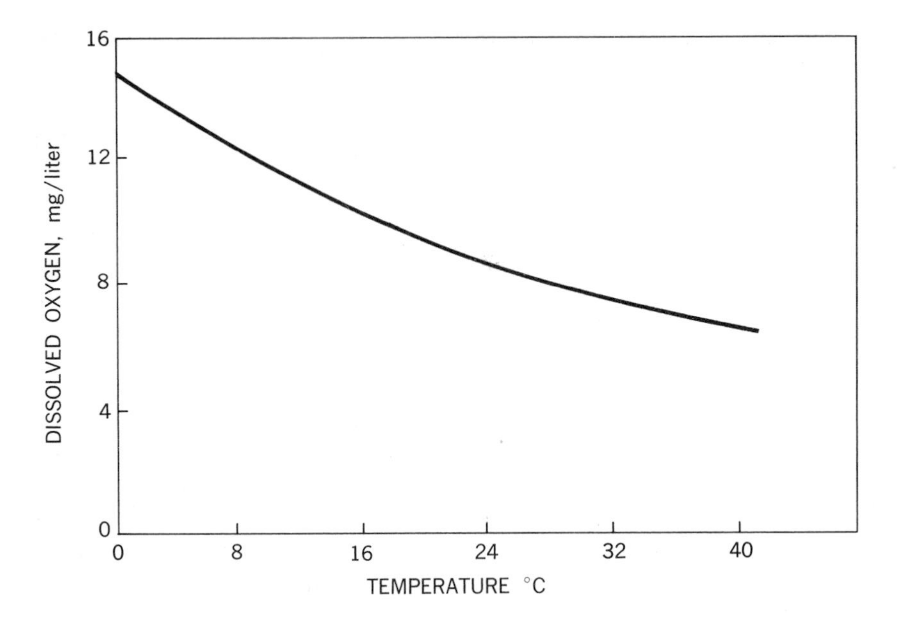

FIGURE 8-7 The Quantity of Oxygen Dissolved in Water Is Related to Temperature. The Higher the Temperature, the Lower the Oxygen Content of the Water. Thermal Pollution Can Lower the Oxygen Content Below the Point Necessary to Sustain Many Animals.

Redrawn from Richard H. Wagner, *Environment and Man* (New York: W. W. Norton & Company, Inc., 1971), p. 137.

Used coolant water frequently may have a temperature 20°F higher than the river or stream to which it is returned. This added heat raises the temperature of the natural waters, with the results that: (1) the amount of dissolved oxygen in the water is decreased; (2) the rates of chemical reactions are increased; (3) false temperature cues are given to aquatic life; and (4) lethal temperature limits may be exceeded.

The decreasing ability of water to contain dissolved oxygen as the temperature increases is shown graphically in Fig. 8-7. Some of the effects of low dissolved oxygen levels on bodies of water were discussed earlier under "oxygen-demanding wastes."

The addition of heated water to a cooler body of water may accelerate the lowering of DO levels because of density differences between the two. The less dense warm water tends to form a layer on top of the cooler, more dense water. This takes place particularly when the body of cool receiving water is deep. The resulting blanket of "hot" water cannot dissolve as much atmospheric oxygen as the underlying cold water, which is denied contact with the atmosphere. Normal biological reduction of the DO level of the atmospherically unreplenished lower layer may lead to anaerobic conditions.

Another effect of this stratification may show up downstream from a dam when the oxygen deficient lower level is discharged through the lower gates of a dam. Serious effects on downstream fish life may result. Also, the ability of the stream below the dam to assimilate oxygen-demanding wastes will be curtailed.

The effects of heat in water are sometimes seen in nature independent of man's interference. On hot summer days the temperature of shallow waters sometimes reaches a point which prevents a DO level sufficient to support some life. Under these conditions, suffocated fish are often found on the surface.

A rough rule of thumb often used by chemists is that the rate of any chemical reaction, including those of respiration and oxidation, approximately doubles with every 10°C (18°F) increase in temperature. In thermally polluted water, fish require more oxygen because of an increased respiration rate. However, the available oxygen in such water has been decreased. Thus, thermal pollution affects fish in a double-barreled fashion.

Other reactions are also influenced. Trout eggs hatch in 165 days when incubated at 37°F. When water temperatures are 54°F, only 32 days are required, and no hatching occurs at water temperatures in excess of 59°F. Such a result can be disastrous to fish populations. If the fish hatch early and find no natural food organisms available, they of course do not survive. The natural food of such hatchlings depends on a food chain originating with plants whose abundance is a function of day length as well as temperature.

The life cycle and natural processes of many aquatic organisms are closely and delicately geared to water temperature. Fish often migrate, spawn, and are otherwise distributed in response to water temperature cues. Shellfish, such as oysters, spawn within a few hours after their environment reaches a critical temperature. These normal life patterns of aquatic organisms can be completely disrupted by artificial changes in water temperatures.

Fish vary widely in their water temperature preferences. An indication of this is the commonly used classification of fish as either cold- or warm-water species. An upper, lethal, temperature limit exists for each species. These limits are given for a number of fish in Fig. 8-8 (see following page), along with the limits recommended by the Federal Water Pollution Control Administration for normal growth and spawning. It is known that temperatures well below the lethal value can cause stress in organisms; hence the much lower recommended values. Lethal limits can be exceeded, in some instances, under conditions of warm water waste discharge.

Another factor to be considered in addition to the temperature change is the rapidity with which the change takes place. Fish are able to acclimate themselves to moderate temperature changes (below lethal levels) if the change is not a sudden one. Normally a moderate temperature change over a 30–40 hour period can be handled by the fish. For example, 95% of the eggs of largemouth bass perish when suddenly transferred from water at 65–70°F into water at 85°F. However, if similar eggs are placed in water and the temperature gradually increased to 85°F over a 30–40 hour time period, 80% of the eggs survive.

An additional threat to aquatic life is created by the common practice of chlorinating coolant water prior to use. This is done to prevent bacterial

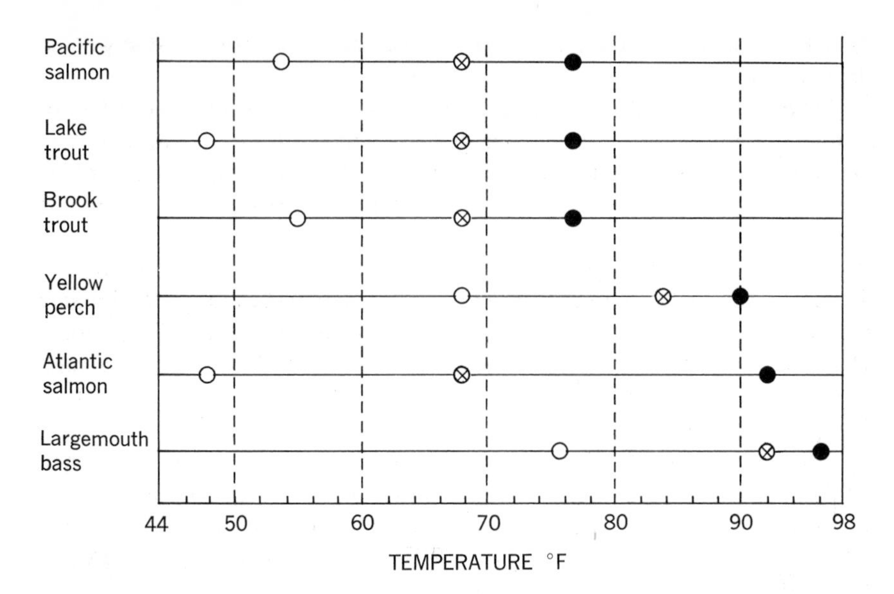

● Upper lethal limit

⊗ Upper limit recommended by Federal Water Pollution Control Administration for satisfactory growth

○ Upper limit recommended by Federal Water Pollution Control Administration for spawning

FIGURE 8-8 WATER TEMPERATURE LETHAL LIMITS

Data selected from more extensive table in *Man and the Ecosphere* (San Francisco: W. H. Freeman and Co., 1971), p. 168.

growths that clog pipes. The chlorine affects organisms in the area receiving the used water until dilution occurs. The chlorine kills microorganisms important in some food chains and may in this way exert a negative influence on fish populations.

A problem of thermal pollution not related to aquatic life is the reduced cooling capability of warmed waters. This is important because nuclear reactor power sources require about 50% more cooling water for a given temperature increase than similar power plants using fossil fuels, and it appears that nuclear plants will be used extensively in the future.

Various solutions to the thermal pollution problem have been proposed and some are already in use. Several industries have incorporated cooling towers into their operations to remove heat from cooling water before returning it to the natural water supply. Two types of towers, wet and dry, are used. Water is run over baffles in a thin layer in the wet tower. Cool air, entering at the bottom, circulates upward and removes heat from the water. In dry towers, air is forced over water-containing pipes by huge fans. Heat is exchanged by radiation and convection from the pipes.

The use of cooling ponds or lakes is another alternative. These ponds could serve as ice-free wintering areas for waterfowl in northern locations or as a means of extending the range (northward) of certain fish. Both of these are positive results of thermal pollution.

Although many schemes have been presented for using the waste heat in some commercially profitable way, no practical applications have been found. Discharge water is not hot enough to heat buildings, and the cost of transporting it to farms for irrigation purposes is prohibitive even when improved crop production is considered. A more promising idea involves the use of waste heat in desalination plants to aid evaporation processes. At present, this is still only an idea. Indications are that waste heat disposal will continue to be a problem for many years.

Suggestions for Further Reading

Journal Articles

1. Bubeck, R. C. 1971. Runoff of de-icing salt. *Science* 172:1128–30.
2. Clark, J. R. 1969. Thermal pollution and aquatic life. *Scientific American* 220:18–27.
3. Jula, T. F. 1971. Environmental aspects of heavy metal toxicity. *Environmental Affairs* 1:74–90.
4. Ryther, J. H., and Dunstan, W. M. 1971. Nitrogen, phosphorus, and eutrophication in the coastal marine environment. *Science* 171:1008–13.
5. Woodwell, G. M. 1967. Toxic substances and ecological cycles. *Scientific American* 216:24–31.
6. The nuclear industry and air pollution. 1970. *Environmental Science and Technology* 4:392–95.
7. Nuclear power: the social conflict. 1970. *Environmental Science and Technology* 5:404–10.
8. Trace metals: unknown, unseen pollution threat. *Chemical and Engineering News* 49 (no. 29):29–33.

Government Documents

1. Aldrich, S. R. 1970. Is nitrogen fertilizer a threat to environment quality. In *Water pollution—1970*, part 2. Hearings before Committee on Public Works, U.S. Senate, 91st Congress, 2nd session, pp. 769–75.

2. Lambou, V., and Lim, B. 1970. Hazards of arsenic in the environment, with particular reference to the aquatic environment. In *Effects of mercury on man and the environment*, part 2. Hearings before the Committee on Public Works, U.S. Senate, 91st Congress, 2nd session, pp. 487–501.
3. Schroeder, H. A. 1970. Trace elements in the human environment. In *Effects of mercury on man and the environment*, part 3. Hearings before the Committee on Public Works, U.S. Senate, 91st Congress, 2nd session, pp. 692–96.
4. U.S. Dept. of Commerce, 1971. *Acid mine drainage*. Sub-Council Report, National Industrial Pollution Control Council.
5. U.S. Dept. of Commerce. 1971. *Animal slaughtering and processing*. Sub-Council Report, National Industrial Pollution Control Council.
6. U.S. Dept. of Commerce. 1971. *Animal wastes*. Staff Report, National Industrial Pollution Control Council.
7. U.S. Dept of Commerce. 1971. *Wood products*. Sub-Council Report, National Industrial Pollution Control Council.
8. U S. Dept. of the Interior. 1970. *Clean water for the 1970's—a status report*. Federal Water Quality Administration.
9. U.S. Dept. of the Interior. 1968. *Report of the committee on water quality criteria*. Federal Water Pollution Control Administration.
10. Wadleigh, C. H. 1968. *Wastes in relation to agriculture and forestry*. U.S. Dept. of Agriculture Miscellaneous Publication No. 1065.

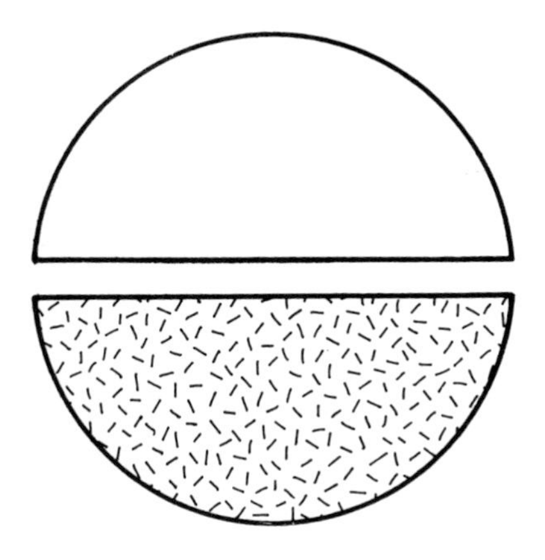

Chapter 9

Mercury

Natural Occurrence and Properties

It is to be expected that some mercury will be present in the environment, because it is a naturally occurring element. Most mercury found in nature is combined with other elements: only rarely is it found in the elemental form. Mercury compounds, like many others, are dispersed throughout rocks, soil, air, water, and living organisms by a complex system of physical, chemical, and biological processes. Table 9-1 (see following page) gives the results of analyses for mercury carried out on various environmental samples as reported by the U.S. Geological Survey.

Mercury and its compounds have been used by man during much of his existence. It is one of the few elements known in biblical times. Its chemical and physical properties make it an attractive metal for use in scientific and industrial applications. These properties are:

1. It is the only metal that is a liquid at room temperature (25°C). Its freezing point, also the lowest for any metal, is −39°C.
2. It has a long liquid range of 396°C which includes all ordinary temperatures. The metal expands uniformly over this range.
3. It has the highest volatility of any metal.
4. The electrical resistivity is very low, causing mercury to be rated as one of the best metallic electrical conductors.
5. Many metals dissolve in mercury to form amalgams (alloys).
6. The metal and its compounds are toxic to all living organisms.

TABLE 9-1 MERCURY LEVELS IN THE ENVIRONMENT

SAMPLE		CONCENTRATION OF Hg (ppm)	COMMENTS
Rock		.01 to 20	Less than 20% of samples had more than 1 ppm. Average value was about 0.1 ppm. Very high values are for organic rich shale.
Soil		0.1	Values varied within very narrow limits.
Air			All samples taken 400 ft. above ground
near a Hg ore deposit		.00009	
near a Cu ore deposit		.00004	
unmineralized area		.00001	
River Water			
65% of samples	less than	.0001	
15% of samples	greater than	.001	
3% of samples	greater than	.005	

Data selected from U.S. Dept. of the Interior, *Mercury in the Environment* (Geological Survey Professional Paper 713), pp. 1, 2, 67.

Nearly all mercury is produced from the sulfide ore cinnabar (HgS) by means of roasting the ore in air. The reaction is:

$$HgS + O_2 \rightarrow Hg + SO_2 \qquad \text{(eq. 9-1)}$$

Mercury is released as a vapor, which is condensed. The other gases are vented into the atmosphere or, hopefully, collected.

The Uses of Mercury by Man

Mercury is used in a wide variety of ways, as illustrated by Table 9-2. The largest user is seen to be the chlor-alkali industry, which produces chlorine (Cl_2) and caustic soda (NaOH) by the electrolysis of salt (NaCl) solutions. Both chemicals produced are very important industrial materials and are made in large quantities annually. The function of mercury in this process is to serve as the cathode of the electrolysis cell. A flowing film of mercury forms an amalgam with sodium metal, which is released from the brine solution at the cathode during electrolysis. The amalgam is removed from the electrolysis cell and reacted with water to form a solution of NaOH. The mercury is recovered for further use. The use of mercury in this application is based on its liquid state, electrical conductivity, and ability to form amalgams

TABLE 9-2 MERCURY CONSUMPTION IN THE UNITED STATES 1969, (IN POUNDS)

AREA OF USE	
Chlor-alkali industry	1,572,000
Electrical apparatus	1,382,000
Paint	739,000
Instrumentation	391,000
Catalysts	221,000
Dental preparations	209,000
Agriculture	204,000
General laboratory use	126,000
Pharmaceuticals	52,000
Pulp and paper making	42,000
Amalgamation	15,000
Others	1,082,000
Total	6,035,000

Adapted from U.S. Senate Subcommittee on Energy, Natural Resources, and the Environment Hearings, *Effects of Mercury on Man and the Environment* (1970), part 2, p. 116.

with sodium metal. The amount of chlorine produced by this method has been steadily increasing since about 1947, as shown by Table 9-3.

The second greatest consumption of mercury occurs in the production of electrical apparatus. This application encompasses a large variety of uses. The mercury vapor lamp used in highway and industrial lighting is one example. These lamps may be installed and operated at lower cost than incandescent lighting and may be operated at desirable high voltages. Other uses include the silent electrical switches used in the home, and mercury batteries. The batteries are characterized by long shelf lives and the ability to operate under conditions of high temperature and humidity.

The use of mercury and its compounds as fungicides constitutes the third largest category of mercury consumption. In this application, use is made of

TABLE 9-3 CHLOR-ALKALI PRODUCTION OF CHLORINE

YEAR	PERCENT OF TOTAL Cl_2 PRODUCED BY METHOD
1947	2
1960	12
1969	34

Data selected from U.S. Senate Subcommittee on Energy, Natural Resources, and the Environment Hearings, *Effects of Mercury on Man and the Environment* (1970), part 2, p. 116.

the toxicity of the substances toward living organisms. These substances are used to destroy fungi in the paint, pulp and paper, and agricultural industries. Mercury compounds are added to paint that is to be used in humid regions to act as a latex preservative and a mildewcide. Paints for use on ships must contain "anti-fouling" agents to prevent barnacle growth. Mercury oxide (HgO) is often used in this application. Mildew proofing of marine paints is also necessary, and phenyl mercuric acetate or its derivatives are commonly used.

This last compound, phenyl mercuric acetate (PMA), is the most important organomercury compound of commerce. Approximately 500,000 lbs. are produced per year. The formula for this widely used substance is

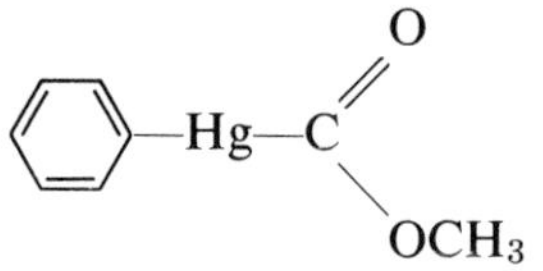

$$C_6H_5\text{—Hg—}C(=O)\text{—}OCH_3$$

The paper and pulp industry has also made use of PMA to prevent the growth of slime on wet paper pulp during processing or storage. Other organomercury compounds have also been used in smaller amounts for the same purpose. The use of organomercury compounds in this area had virtually stopped by 1970 because of a ruling by the Federal Food and Drug Administration barring the use of mercury compounds in paper that might come in contact with food.

Agricultural industries use organomercury compounds as *seed dressings* to inhibit the growth of fungi on agricultural seeds. Some typical compounds used for this are:

methylmercurynitrile $CH_3\text{—Hg—}C\equiv N$

methylmercurydicyandiamide $CH_3\text{—Hg—}N(H)\text{—}C(=NH)\text{—}NHCN$

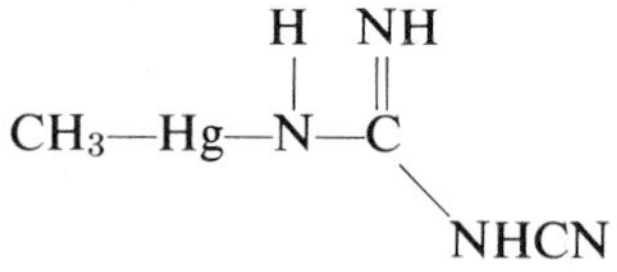

methylmercuryacetate $CH_3\text{—Hg—}C(=O)\text{—}OCH_3$

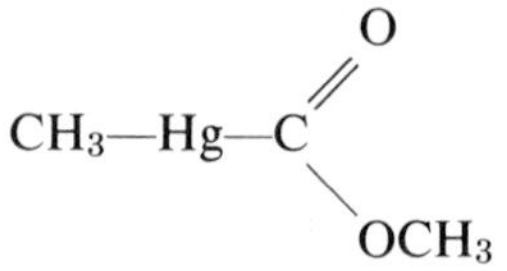

ethylmercurychloride $C_2H_5\text{—Hg—Cl}$

Elemental or metallic mercury is used as a catalyst in some chemical manufacturing processes, particularly in the manufacture of vinyl chloride, the base for many plastics. It was mercury effluent from a vinyl chloride plant that caused the largest known epidemic of mercury poisonings in Minamata Bay, Japan (1953–60). Metallic mercury is also used in thermometers and temperature recording devices because of the long liquid range, uniform and large coefficient of thermal expansion, and electrical conductivity.

Sources of Hg Pollution

Industry is the largest user of newly mined mercury. Since 1970, much has been done to eliminate waste discharges of mercury from industrial sources.

The chlor-alkali industry is the largest industrial user. Theoretically, no mercury is consumed during the process of producing Cl_2 or caustic soda. Actually, however, losses of mercury do take place. Some is lost to the products, some leaves with effluent water, and some is lost through air ventilation systems. The operating conditions of the electrolysis cells result in a loss of 0.1–0.5 lbs. of mercury for every ton of Cl_2 produced. This amounts to an industry-wide amount of 400 tons per year. Most of this loss ultimately shows up in the waste-water discharges from the plants. During 1970, producers were able to reduce these discharges by 86% mainly by recirculating waste water and installing lagoons and settling ponds in which the mercury collects.

The use of PMA by the pulp and paper industry for in-process slime control has essentially ceased. Previously, this use resulted in PMA discharges with waste water. The incineration of paper produced when PMA was used constitutes a possible source of airborne mercury pollution, because trace amounts of mercury remain in such paper. Commercial laundries, particularly those with a diaper service, use PMA to suppress mold.

A current area of great concern is the use of mercury compounds as seed dressings in agriculture. The amount of mercury in the seed dressing formulation is small, but the effect is large, because the seed dressing is applied to a large volume of seed that is subsequently sowed over millions of acres, which results in an extremely widespread dissemination of the mercury compounds. Also, there is evidence suggesting that the mercury undergoes translocation in plants (a serious effect discussed later).

In addition to losses of mercury from direct usage, some is released in the combustion of coal and petroleum products. A number of investigators have found mercury levels averaging about 1 ppm in coal. This amount seems small, but on a worldwide basis the annual world production of fossil fuels of about 5×10^9 metric tons could, upon combustion, release 5000 metric tons of mercury.

Other human activities contribute to mercury levels also. Sludge from sewage plants has been found to contain enough mercury, in some cases, to make it unsuitable for use as a soil fertilizer. Los Angeles and San Diego city effluents contain 1 ppb of mercury despite the fact that no industrial source is known. It is estimated that a population of one million people will discharge into the sewers 1000 pounds of mercury annually. The sources are such commonly used materials as disinfectants, pharmaceuticals, and paints.

Mercury Amplification in Food Chains

Mercury is considered to get into the food chain by two routes, water and seed dressings. The contamination of natural foods by mercury dramatically came to the attention of the public in 1970 with the announcement that abnormally high mercury concentrations were found in fresh water fish from Lake Erie and the St. Clair River and in salt water tuna and swordfish. Abnormally high levels are considered to be those exceeding the FDA-established maximums of 0.5 ppm for food and 0.005 ppm for water.

The report on fresh water fish from Lake Erie and the St. Clair River indicated the presence of mercury at concentrations given in Table 9-4. These concentrations are based on the net weight of the edible portions. Both tuna and swordfish were reported to contain as much as 1 ppm Hg, but the FDA reported that only a few tuna had concentrations in excess of the legal limit. A higher percentage of the swordfish tested were over the established levels. The FDA results for tuna indicated an average mercury content of 0.25 ppm for large fish (over 50 lbs.) and an average of 0.13 for small tuna (under 26 lbs.).

TABLE 9-4 MERCURY LEVELS IN FRESHWATER FISH

FISH	MERCURY LEVEL (ppm)
Walleye pike	1.4 to 3.57
Sucker	0.88
Northern pike	0.64
White bass	0.53 to 0.80
Channel catfish	0.32 to 1.80
Coho salmon	0.24 to 0.96
Carp	0.08 to 0.28

Adapted from U.S. Dept. of Commerce, *Mercury* (Staff Report of National Industrial Pollution Control Council), p. 10.

Further studies on fish have shown that all fish not directly exposed to mercury during their growth still consistently have mercury levels in the low range of 0.005–0.075 ppm. Further, the rates of mercury accumulation varied significantly with different conditions and between different organs. The results of studies into the effects of water-borne mercury on rainbow trout are given in Table 9-5. In this 1969 study, trout were exposed to nonlethal mercury concentrations for 1 hour per day over a 10-day period. After 10 days some trout were sacrificed and analyzed. The analysis results are given in Table 9-5. The remaining fish were kept in mercury-free water and, after 45 weeks, the mercury had been eliminated from all except the liver and kidney tissues, which still retained levels of 1.8 and 12.3 ppm respectively.

Another fact determined by studies involving fish is that most of the mercury present in living tissues is in the form of organic compounds and

TABLE 9-5 MERCURY LEVELS IN TROUT TISSUES

TISSUE	MERCURY LEVEL (ppm)
Blood	22.8
Kidney	17.3
Liver	16.7
Brain	10.1
Gonad	4.1
Muscle	4.0

Adapted from U.S. Dept. of the Interior, *Mercury in the Environment* (Geological Survey Professional Paper 713), p. 33.

primarily in the form of methyl mercury. The significance of this fact will become apparent later in this chapter.

It is becoming evident that mercury, although not an essential mineral to the body, is concentrated in living tissues. This concentration process involves food chains in which small organisms containing mercury are ingested in quantity by larger organisms, which, in turn, are eaten by still larger ones and so on. The organisms further up the chain get all the mercury collected by those down the chain. This amplification can result in high levels of mercury in the tissues of animals near the top of the chain. Man is at the top of every food chain in which he is involved.

In the case of fish, tiny marine diatoms have mercury compounds adsorbed to their surfaces. Fish, upon eating these or other small animals or plants, concentrate the mercury in their tissues. Some mercury is also absorbed by fish through their gills from surrounding water. As a result of this process, the tissue of the fish has a higher mercury level than the surrounding water. For example, trout exposed to mercury levels of 0.1 ppm for 1 hour per day had a tissue level of 4 ppm of mercury after 10 days exposure.

Some evidence indicates that mercury from seed dressings can undergo translocation in plants and animals. Translocation in plants involves the transfer of mercury from seed to crop. In animals, the process causes mercury to move to various parts of the animal or into products obtained from the animal (eggs, for example). It is possible for mercury to be translocated from grain seed to the harvested grain, then to a hen, and finally to eggs. Data exist to support this idea. Barley and oats were both grown from untreated seed and from seed that had received a dressing containing methyl mercury. The resulting crops were fed to hens, which then produced eggs. The experimental results are given in Table 9-6.

Another comparison illustrates the translocation phenomenon as well. In Sweden, methyl mercury was used as a seed dressing (it is now banned), while in Denmark no mercury was involved. A comparison of mercury levels in meat products obtained from animals which were fed the resulting grain is given in Table 9-7.

TABLE 9-6 TRANSLOCATION OF MERCURY

UNTREATED SEEDS	TREATED SEEDS
Hg concentration of resulting crop was 0.014 ppm.	Hg concentration of resulting crop was 0.030 ppm.
Hg concentration of eggs from hens fed on the crop was 0.008–0.012 ppm.	Hg concentration of eggs from hens fed on the crop was 0.022–0.029 ppm.

Data selected from *Environment* 11:13 (May 1969).

In both examples given above it should be noted that in no instance has the level of mercury reached the limit of 0.5 ppm. The point is that mercury from seeds does appear in grain through translocation and eventually finds its way into animal tissue by way of food chains.

TABLE 9-7 TRANSLOCATION OF MERCURY, EFFECTS ON MEAT

MEAT PRODUCT (RAW)	CONCENTRATION OF MERCURY (ppm)	
	Swedish	Danish
Pork chops	0.030	0.003
Beef	0.012	0.003
Bacon	0.018	0.004
Pig liver	0.060	0.009
Ox liver	0.016	0.005

Adapted from *Environment* 11:13 (May 1969).

Mercury Poisoning and Biological Methylation

The occurrence of mercury poisonings is a well-documented fact. Widespread incidents have been reported only during the last two decades. Five major instances of mercury poisoning are listed in Table 9-8. These incidents resulted

TABLE 9-8 MAJOR MERCURY POISONINGS

LOCATION	YEAR	RESULTS
Minamata Bay, Japan	1953–60	111 dead or seriously injured
Iraq	1961	35 dead, 321 injured
West Pakistan	1963	4 dead, 34 injured
Guatemala	1966	20 dead, 45 injured
Nigata, Japan	1968	5 dead, 25 injured

Data selected from U.S. Senate Subcommittee on Energy, Natural Resources, and the Environment Hearings, *Effects of Mercury on Man and the Environment* (1970), part 2, p. 110.

from the eating of mercury-contaminated fish or the eating of seed grain treated with mercury compounds.

Although the toxic action of mercury in the body is not completely understood, recent research has provided some information about the problem. The primary facts determined are:

1. All mercury compounds are toxic to the body when present in sufficient quantity.
2. Different mercury compounds exhibit somewhat different characteristics of toxicity, distribution, accumulation, and retention times in the body.
3. Certain biological transformations may take place in the environment or the body which change mercury compounds of one type into other types.
4. The ultimate effects of mercury in the body appear to be inhibition of enzyme action and cellular damage caused by the ability of mercury to bind tightly with sulfur-containing groups in molecules which are present in both enzymes and cell walls. Such binding inactivates enzymes and upsets chemical reactions which they catalyze in the body. The membrane properties of cell walls are disrupted by the binding of mercury, and normal cellular activities are inhibited.
5. The damage done to the body by mercury is usually permanent. There is no known effective treatment.

The behavior of mercury compounds in the body is usually discussed in terms of three different classes of mercury compounds. Inorganic mercury includes elemental (metallic) mercury and its salts, such as chlorides, oxides, and so forth. Organic mercury compounds constitute the two other classes. The arylmercurials contain aromatic hydrocarbons as part of the molecule, while alkylmercurials contain aliphatic hydrocarbons.

Inorganic mercury tends to accumulate in liver and kidney tissue. This causes damage, but also provides a means for rapid elimination through the urinary system. Metallic mercury vapor has a great capacity for diffusion through the lungs into the blood and then into the brain, where serious central nervous system damage takes place. Normally, inorganic mercury, in the form of compounds, does not remain in the body long enough to accumulate to dangerous levels.

Upon introduction into the body, arylmercurials appear to break down readily into inorganic mercury compounds and behave as indicated above. The compound PMA, previously discussed, behaves this way.

Alkylmercurials represent the greatest health hazard for a number of reasons:

1. They easily penetrate into and accumulate in brain tissue. This is accomplished in part because they diffuse easily through biological membranes.
2. They exhibit long retention times in the body. This enables the mercury concentration to build up even though dosages may be low. The estimated half-life of these compounds in the body is 70 days.

3. Alkylmercurials can be produced from inorganic mercury by the action of certain anaerobic microorganisms. This transformation has been found to take place readily in the mud of rivers and lakes. The extent to which it occurs in the human body is not known, but microorganisms found in some animal intestines are able to accomplish the feat.

The classes of mercury and their relationships to each other are summarized in Fig. 9-1.

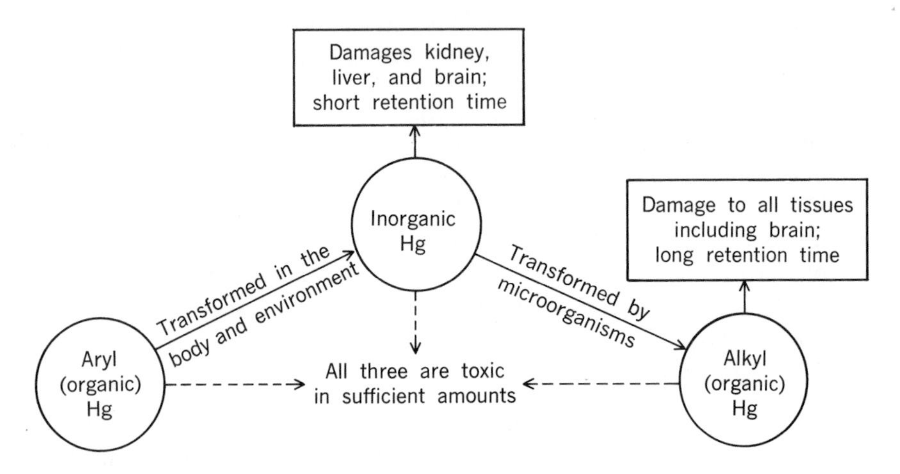

FIGURE 9-1 RELATIONSHIPS BETWEEN CLASSES OF TOXIC MERCURY

Redrawn, with modifications, from *Environment* (May 1969), p. 13.

Methylmercurials, which appear to be the most dangerous and toxic of the mercury compounds, can enter the environment in several ways—directly, indirectly, intentionally, or unintentionally. A direct and intentional route is represented by the use of methylmercurials on seed. A direct but unintentional route is provided when methylmercurials used in industry or formed as a waste product of industrial processes are dumped into natural waters. The episode at Minamata Bay was caused in this way. An indirect route is provided when other mercury compounds are methylated (transformed) by biological organisms.

A very serious example of the latter route involves inorganic and phenyl mercury from industrial sources. The metallic mercury or compound, upon settling into the bottom mud of lakes, is converted by anaerobic microorganisms into CH_3Hg^+ or $(CH_3)_2Hg$. This latter compound is very volatile and escapes from the mud into the water. The $(CH_3)_2Hg$ is stable in alkaline solutions, but when exposed to acidic surroundings, it changes to CH_3Hg^+. This ion is soluble in water and concentrates in living organisms, usually appearing in body lipids. This accumulation is the result of direct absorption of the ion or an amplification by a food chain process.

Solutions to the Mercury Pollution Problem

Sources of environmental mercury are easily documented, but a close examination reveals the complexity of dealing with mercury pollution. The complexity is illustrated by the following facts:

1. Mercury is volatile and can contaminate the air.
2. Mercury is a liquid and can spread over surfaces in small droplets, which prove very difficult to collect.
3. Mercurials undergo translocation in plants and animals.
4. Mercury or mercury compounds can be converted by microorganisms, present in river and lake mud, into highly toxic methyl mercury compounds which are amplified by common food chains, including man's.

A 1971 report of the U.S. Environmental Protection Agency contained the following recommendations for the prevention of further environmental pollution by mercury:

1. The use of all alkyl mercury pesticides should be terminated.
2. The use of all other mercurial pesticides should be restricted to areas of demonstrated need.
3. All industrial users of mercury should be required to reduce discharges of mercury into the environment to levels approximating normal background levels.

The implementation of these recommendations will not completely solve the problem. Sufficient mercury contamination is present in the bottom muds of rivers and lakes to continue to yield highly toxic CH_3Hg^+ into the waters for years to come. Some sort of decontamination is needed. Large scale pilot experiments on decontamination methods have been recommended.

Three methods for decontamination are now under study in Sweden:

1. Bottom sediments are covered with fresh, finely divided materials having high absorption capabilities.
2. Bottom sediments are buried under inorganic, inert materials.
3. The mercury-containing bottom sediments are to be removed by dredging or pumping.

Suggestions for Further Reading

Journal Articles

1. Aaronson, T. 1971. Mercury in the environment. *Environment* 13 (no. 4):16–23.
2. Goldwater, L. 1971. Mercury in the environment. *Scientific American* 224:15–21.

3. Grant, N. 1969. Legacy of the mad hatter. *Environment* 11 (no. 4):18–23, 43–44.
4. Grant, N. 1971. Mercury in man. *Environment* 13 (no. 4):2–15.
5. Hammond, A. L. 1971. Mercury in the environment: natural and human factors. *Science* 171:788–89.
6. Joensuu, O. I. 1971. Fossil fuels as a source of mercury pollution. *Science* 172:1027–28.
7. Löfroth, G. 1969. Birds give warning. *Environment* 11 (no. 4):10–17.
8. Novick, S. 1969. A new pollution problem. *Environment* 11 (no. 4):2–9.
9. Staff Report. 1971. Mercury in the air. *Environment* 13 (no. 4):24, 29–33.
10. Mercury: anatomy of a pollution problem. *Chemical and Engineering News* 49 (no. 27):22–34.

Government Documents

1. U.S Dept. of the Interior. 1970. *Mercury in the environment.* Geological Survey Profession Paper 713.
2. U.S. Dept. of Commerce. 1970. *Mercury.* Staff Report, National Industrial Pollution Control Council.
3. Löfroth, G 1970. Methylmercury. Ecological Research Committee, Bulletin No. 4, Swedish Natural Science Research Council, 1969. In *Water pollution—1970,* part 2. Hearings before Committee on Public Works, U.S. Senate, 91st Congress, 2nd session, pp. 676–716.

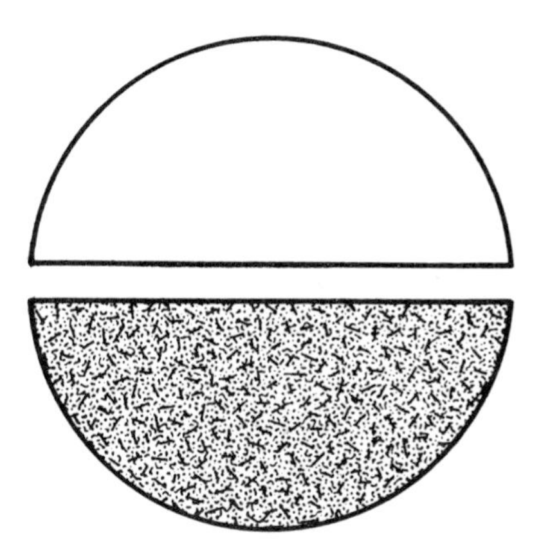

Chapter 10

Lead

Introduction

Lead pollution is a problem involving air, water, and soil. For convenience, our entire consideration of lead will be included in this single chapter. Actually, lead pollution is increasing more rapidly in the air than in soil and water, but historically it has been dealt with as a water problem.

The earth's crust does not contain a particularly large amount of lead (about $2 \times 10^{-5}\%$). Through geological processes, it has been concentrated into ore deposits from which the metal is obtained. Soil generally contains small quantities of lead compounds.

The lead concentration of an area has been found to depend upon the geology of the area and the proximity to sources of lead pollution. The average lead content of the earth's crust in parts per million is 16; however, levels of several thousand ppm can be found near smelters.

The natural background level of lead and its compounds in air should be very low because of low vapor-pressure values. Temperatures in excess of 800°C are necessary for lead or its common compounds to reach a vapor pressure of 1 torr. By contrast, mercury has a vapor pressure of 1 torr at 126°C.

Properties and Uses of Lead

An estimated 1.4 million tons of lead were consumed in the United States during 1969. The demand and uses of the metal are related to a number of its properties including the following:

1. Lead has a low melting point, which allows the use of simple, inexpensive techniques when handling it as a liquid.
2. It is a soft, malleable metal that is easily formed into a variety of shapes.
3. The chemical activity of lead causes a protective coating to form upon exposure to moist air.
4. Lead has the ability to form alloys with many other metals. The resultant alloys have properties different from those of pure lead.
5. The density of lead is greater than any other common metal except gold and mercury.

The quantities of lead used in various applications are given in Table 10-1. The production of lead storage batteries for automobile use consumes the largest quantity of lead annually. Both metallic lead and its compounds are used in this application. The electrodes of a typical battery contain an inactive supportive structure called a grid. This structure is made of a lead alloy containing 93% lead and 7% antimony. It provides mechanical support for the active battery ingredients and a path for the electrical current. The active portions of the battery consist of lead dioxide (PbO_2) and lead metal, which are bonded to the grid.

TABLE 10-1 QUANTITIES OF LEAD USED—1969

APPLICATION	TONS USED	PERCENTAGE OF TOTAL USED
Storage batteries	582,546	43.1
Metal products	354,411	26.2
Chemicals	271,730	20.1
Pigments	101,185	7.5
Miscellaneous	42,103	3.1
Total	1,351,975	100.0

Adapted from U.S. Dept. of the Interior, *Minerals Yearbook—1969*, p. 638.

During 1969, 46.4 million lead storage batteries were produced. New equipment (mainly automobiles) consumed 10.1 million, 35.5 million replaced old or worn out units, and 0.8 million were exported.

Many metal products contain lead. A partial list consists of:

1. Ammunition
2. Bearing metal
3. Cable covering
4. Caulking substances
5. Pipes, traps, and bends (plumbing)
6. Sheet lead
7. Solder
8. Type metal

Some of these products are made from pure lead that is cast, rolled, or extruded into various shapes. Most, however, are made from lead alloys. Solder contains 50–95% lead, the remainder being tin. The melting point of solder changes with the composition. Type metal, used in the printing industry, is an alloy of lead, tin, and antimony. A common formulation used in type metal contains 85% lead, 12% antimony, and 3% tin. Bearing metal is an alloy containing lead and antimony. Lead shot contains 0.1–0.2% arsenic, added to increase hardness and the spherical nature. Low-melting alloys, for use in fire alarms, automatic fire sprinklers, and electrical fuses, are alloys of lead containing bismuth, cadmium, or mercury. The melting point of the alloy is determined by the composition.

The use of nonalloyed lead is primarily limited to products that must resist corrosion. Pure lead is used in pipe designed to carry corrosive chemicals, in sheets used to line sinks or vats exposed to corrosive substances, and as a covering for electrical cable used underground or under water.

Of the 271,730 tons of lead used in the manufacture of chemicals, 271,128 tons or 99.8% went into the production of a single compound, tetraethyl lead, the popular anti-knock additive for gasoline.

Lead compounds are used as paint pigments because they have low water solubilities, good covering power, and they exist in a variety of colors. The most widely used compound is "white lead," $Pb(OH)_2 \cdot 2PbCO_3$. "Red lead," Pb_3O_4, is a bright red powder used as a pigment in corrosion-resistant paints. An attractive yellow color is produced by the inclusion of "chrome yellow," $PbCrO_4$, in paint formulations.

An interesting use of lead, classified in Table 10-1 as miscellaneous, is the production of pottery glaze. A glaze is a thin layer of glass fused onto the surface of clay objects. The main ingredient of ceramic glazes is silica, which combines with other oxides to give complex silicates (glasses). The lead compound PbO is added because it gives the final glaze attractive properties unattainable with other oxides.

Sources of Airborne Lead Pollution

The amount of lead in the air has increased markedly as the result of man's activities. This fact is dramatically demonstrated by a 1969 study of ice from northern Greenland. Samples of ice taken from various depths were analyzed for lead. The sampling depth was related to the year during which the sample was deposited as snow. Some results of this study are shown in Fig. 10-1 (see following page). As noted in the figure, lead levels in the ice (corresponding to atmospheric levels) have increased markedly since the industrial revolution and very sharply since 1940. A similar study of south pole ice sheets found the lead level too low for detection prior to 1940. Levels of 0.02 $\mu g/kg$ have been detected in very new ice.

Atmospheric lead concentrations in urban areas are 5–50 times that of

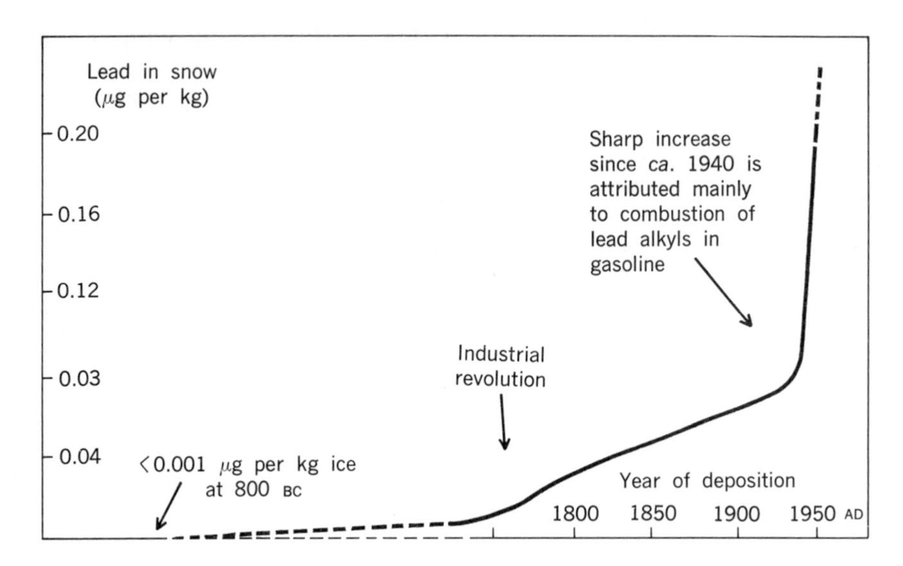

FIGURE 10-1 LEAD CONTENT OF GREENLAND ICE

Redrawn, with permission, from D. Bryce-Smith, "Lead Pollution—A Growing Hazard to Public Health," *Chemistry in Britain* 7:55 (1971).

nonurban areas. This variation of atmospheric lead with location is given in Table 10-2 which contains values of average lead concentrations from numerous reporting sites. It is interesting that the lead concentration in ambient air of most major American cities has not increased appreciably in the past 15 years, despite increased lead emissions. This "steady-state" situation is apparently the result of dispersion to remote areas (where levels are increasing) and the existence of natural mechanisms that remove lead from the atmosphere.

TABLE 10-2 AMBIENT AIR LEAD CONCENTRATION

TYPE OF LOCATION	NUMBER OF REPORTING SITES	AMBIENT AIR LEAD CONC. ($\mu g/m^3$)
Urban	217	1.11
Non-urban—near	5	.21
Non-urban—intermediate	15	.096
Non-urban—remote	10	.022

Adapted from U.S. Senate Subcommittee on Energy, Natural Resources, and the Environment Hearings, *Effects of Mercury on Man and the Environment* (1970), part 3, p. 673.

Lead emissions into the atmosphere are of two types, particulates and gaseous compounds. Gaseous emissions are generated primarily by the combustion of gasoline additives, tetraethyl lead and tetramethyl lead, in automobile engines. Particulates represent the form of emissions from most other sources. Table 10-3 contains estimated lead emissions by source for the U.S. during 1968.

TABLE 10-3 ATMOSPHERIC LEAD SOURCES—1968

SOURCE	LEAD EMITTED (TONS/YEAR)
Gasoline combustion	181,000
Coal combustion	920
Fuel oil combustion	24
Lead alkyl manufacturing	810
Primary lead smelting	174
Secondary lead smelting	811
Brass manufacturing	521
Lead oxide manufacturing	20
Gasoline transfer	36
Total	184,316

Data selected from U.S. Senate Subcommittee on Energy, Natural Resources, and the Environment Hearings, *Effects of Mercury on Man and the Environment* (1970), part 3, p. 673.

One fact stands out from these data. Gasoline combustion accounts for the vast majority (98.2%) of all atmospheric lead pollution. The need for lead containing additives in gasoline was discussed in Chapter 2. The chemical route followed by these additives during gasoline combustion results in the emission of many different lead compounds in automobile exhaust. The two principal lead compounds emitted are PbBrCl and $PbBrCl \cdot 2PbO$.

Halogen containing compounds are formed because of the presence of chemical scavengers in the anti-knock fluid added to gasoline. The active anti-knock agents in the fluid are tetraethyl lead [$Pb(C_2H_5)_4$], tetramethyl lead [$Pb(CH_3)_4$), or a combination of both. Scavengers are added to chemically combine with any lead compounds left in the engine as a result of combustion of the anti-knock agents. These compounds, which would change to engine-damaging metallic lead if left behind, react with the scavengers and form compounds that are gases at operating engine temperatures. These gaseous compounds then exit with the rest of the exhaust products. The two main scavengers used are ethylene dibromide ($C_2H_4Br_2$) and ethylene dichloride ($C_2H_4Cl_2$). A typical additive mix for automobile gasoline contains 62% tetraethyl lead, 18% ethylenedibromide, 18% ethylenedichloride, and 2% other ingredients.

The variety and relative amounts of lead products contained in automobile exhaust are shown in Table 10-4. The first column shows the amount of each lead compound present in exhaust immediately following discharge. The second column shows the amount of each compound present 18 hours after discharge. The 18-hour figures indicate that the lead compounds probably undergo reactions when released into the atmosphere, since they were obtained by collecting the exhaust in a black bag filled with clean dry air and then analyzing the mixture 18 hours later. These results indicate that lead carbonates, oxycarbonates, and oxides are important substances to consider when the health effects of lead pollution are investigated.

TABLE 10-4 LEAD COMPOUNDS IN AUTO EXHAUST

	PERCENTAGE OF TOTAL LEAD PARTICLES COUNTED IN EXHAUST	
LEAD COMPOUND	Zero Time	After 18 Hours
PbBrCl	32.0	12.0
PbBrCl·2PbO	31.4	1.6
$PbCl_2$	10.7	8.3
Pb(OH)Cl	7.7	7.2
$PbBr_2$	5.5	0.5
$PbCl_2 \cdot 2PbO$	5.2	5.6
Pb(OH)Br	2.2	0.1
PbO_x	2.2	21.2
$PbCO_3$	1.2	13.8
$PbBr_2 \cdot 2PbO$	1.1	0.1
$PbCO_3 \cdot 2PbO$	1.0	29.6

Redrawn, with permission, from part of a table in *Nature* 232:553 (1971).

Although major attention has been given to the contribution of gasoline combustion to atmospheric lead pollution, the other sources given in Table 10-2 should not be overlooked. Though they contribute only a small percentage of the total lead pollution, they can become extremely important as point-sources in localized areas. Smelters can produce high levels of lead in air and soils located in their immediate vicinity. Concentrations of lead as high as several milligrams per cubic meter have been observed at ground level downwind from smelters.

Sources of Water-borne Lead Pollution

Public water supplies in the U.S. rarely contain clinically significant quantities of lead. The upper concentration limit for lead in water has been established by the Public Health Service as 0.05 mg/ℓ. In one recent 5-year summary (1962–1967) sponsored by the Federal Water Pollution Control Administration, the maximum lead concentration in rivers and lakes sampled was 0.140 mg/ℓ. Only 2 percent (27 of 1700 samples) contained lead in excess of the PHS limit. Most samples with high levels were taken from waters located near metal working industries.

Some serious outbreaks of lead poisoning took place in Europe a number of years ago. The source of the lead was found to be lead pipe used in interior and exterior plumbing. Very little difficulty of this type is common in the U.S. because iron pipe is used in exterior water distribution systems, and galvanized iron or copper pipes are used in residences. A slight danger might exist in very old homes in which lead plumbing was used. Actually, lead plumbing would be harmless when used with most natural waters because of water hardness. These hard waters contain carbonate ($CO_3^=$) and sulfate ($SO_4^=$) ions which react with lead to form a water-insoluble protective coating of $PbCO_3$ and $PbSO_4$.

Two problems similar to the one of lead in water have recently become of interest. These problems involve moonshine whiskey and glazed ceramic containers.

The consumption of illegally produced whiskey is a cause of lead poisoning in some parts of the country. In 1969, 30% of the illegal whiskey samples taken by the Atlanta regional office of the Federal Alcohol and Tobacco Tax Unit contained more than 1 mg of lead per liter. This is 20 times the legal limit set by the Public Health Service for water. The source of this lead in moonshine whiskey is lead solder used in the tubing of distillation units, and lead-containing automobile radiators used as condensers.

Lead-containing ceramic glazes are a serious source of lead poisoning when used on containers for foodstuffs. The use of such glazes on ceramics was discussed earlier: it has been found that highly acidic liquids such as apple juice may dissolve the glaze and release lead into the liquid if the glaze is not properly formulated and applied.

A two-year-old Montreal boy died in 1970 as a result of drinking apple juice left standing in a handmade earthenware jug. Subsequent tests showed that juice left in the jug for 3 hours acquired a lead concentration of 157 mg/ℓ. After 3 days the level was 1300 mg/ℓ.

As a result of the death, 264 contemporary earthenware vessels were checked, and 50% released sufficient lead to make them unsafe for culinary use. Ten to 25% were capable of causing severe lead poisoning. Similar tests were run on 117 ceramic samples with unknown glaze compositions. The amount of lead extracted in the tests is given in Table 10-5. The United States FDA has recently defined 7 ppm as the maximum allowable amount of lead released from glazes intended for use with food or drink.

Lead in the Diet

The diet appears to be the principal source of lead for the general population. All natural foods contain small quantities of lead, and some additional lead may be picked up during the preparation of foods. Acidic foods in particular can leach lead from cooking, serving, and storage utensils made from lead-containing alloys or glazed pottery.

Soils in some areas are still heavily contaminated with the stable com-

TABLE 10-5 CERAMIC GLAZE AS A SOURCE OF LEAD

CONCENTRATION OF LEAD RELEASED (mg/ℓ or ppm)	NUMBER AND SOURCE OF ARTICLES GIVING UP LEAD		
	Imported Pottery	Domestic Commercial Ware	Domestic Handcrafted
Less than 0.5	9	17	10
0.5–0.7	5	7	4
7–20	6	4	4
20–100	6	15	6
Greater than 100	3	5	16

Modified, with permission, from table in *The New England Journal of Medicine* 283:671 (1970).

pound lead arsenate, which was a widely used pesticide prior to World War II. Its use has been discontinued in favor of organic pesticides in many areas.

Limited studies of crops growing near highways suggest that, other variables being equal, lead levels in plants decrease exponentially with distance from highways, which provides more evidence against the automobile.

Another dietary problem is possible among small children who are known to have a penchant for nibbling on materials not normally considered part of a well-rounded diet. Prior to 1940, lead was commonly used as an ingredient of interior house paint. Today nontoxic titanium compounds are used for interior paints, and lead is restricted to exterior use. Children living in pre-1940 structures have suffered lead poisoning from eating flaking paint. A piece of such paint the size of an adult's thumbnail contains 50–100 mg of lead. Children between the ages of 1 and 6 years are the main victims, and 85–90% of the cases involve youngsters in the 1–3 year age group.

A serious dietary problem is created when wild waterfowl ingest spent lead buckshot. The situation is alarming in some areas: the resulting lead toxemia is responsible for an estimated 2–3% loss of waterfowl annually. The heaviest duck mortality from this source has occurred along the Mississippi flyway.

A typical shot shell contains 280 pellets of number 6 shot, and an average of 5 shells, or 1400 pellets, are expended for each duck taken. These pellets are released primarily into the water and end up in the bottom muds. According to one count, more than 118,000 pellets were found per acre on the bottom of Wisconsin's Lake Puckaway. The species most heavily affected have been such bottom-feeders as mallards and pintails. The ingested lead is changed into soluble lead salts, which apparently paralyze the gizzard. Death by starvation then occurs within a month. In acute cases, death may occur in one or two weeks.

The Behavior of Lead in the Body

The chemical form of lead is an important factor affecting its biological behavior in the body. Organic lead compounds, such as tetraethyl lead, are readily absorbed by the body through the skin or mucous membranes. This is a serious problem only to a small group of occupationally exposed workers, such as those involved in the manufacture of such compounds. Lead compounds used in gasoline, although organic, are not pollution hazards in the organic form because they are changed to inorganic forms during gasoline combustion. They are released into the atmosphere as these less hazardous compounds. Inorganic lead is absorbed primarily through the gastrointestinal and respiratory tracts and is the main source of lead for the body.

Not all inhaled or ingested lead is absorbed or retained by the body. Approximately 5–10% of that ingested is absorbed from the gastrointestinal tract, and about 30% of that inhaled is absorbed from the respiratory tract. Of the 30% absorbed through respiration, only 5% is retained, and this amount is a function of particle size of the inhaled material.

The toxic action of lead in the body has been traced in part to an enzyme inhibition by the Pb^{+2} ion. The inhibited enzyme is one necessary for the formation of hemoglobin. The inhibition is the result of a strong interaction between Pb^{+2} and the sulfur groups of some amino acids of the enzyme. This may not be the only toxic effect.

The lead retained in the body from both air and dietary sources accumulates predominantly in the skeleton (90–95%). The bones serve as accumulation sites because of similarities between the Ca^{+2} ions of bones and the Pb^{+2} ions. The total lead body pool for a 150 lb. man is 100–400 milligrams.

Evidence obtained from animal experiments suggests that there is a continuous turnover of lead in the body, so measured concentrations tend to reflect the current degree of exposure. The biological half-life of lead in human bones is estimated to be 2–3 years.

An unpleasant aspect of bone-accumulated lead is that it may be remobilized and sent to other parts of the body long after the initial absorption. This remobilization can occur during feverish illness, as a result of cortisone treatment and as a result of old age.

Because the determination of lead in bones is difficult, the concentration of lead in blood or urine is commonly used as an indication of total lead in the body. The blood level appears to be a more reliable indicator than the urine level. Estimates vary concerning the exact level of lead in the blood necessary to cause the appearance of the symptoms of clinical lead poisoning (plumbism). In adults these levels are usually in the range of 60 to 100 micrograms (μg) per 100 ml of blood.

Table 10-6 gives standards for occupationally exposed adults. The lead concentrations in blood are divided into four categories—normal, acceptable, excessive, and dangerous. The significance of these categories becomes ap-

TABLE 10-6 FOUR CATEGORIES OF BLOOD LEAD CONCENTRATIONS IN ADULTS

CATEGORY	BLOOD LEAD LEVEL (μg per 100 mℓ)	DESCRIPTION
A (normal)	<40	'Normal' population with no occupational or abnormal exposure.
B (acceptable)	40–80	Increased absorption resulting from occupational or abnormal exposure which is occupationally acceptable.
C (excessive)	80–120	Increased absorption from excessive occupational or other exposure which may be associated with mild symptoms or signs, or, rarely, with severe symptoms or signs. These levels are unacceptable.
D (dangerous)	>120	Dangerous absorption from occupational or other exposure in which mild and severe symptoms and also long-term after-effects are increasingly probable.

Adapted from *Chemistry in Britain* 7:162 (1971).

parent when the lead levels are compared to those found in blood samples collected from various segments of the general population. A study conducted among adults living near a major freeway in California found average blood lead levels of 22.7 μg/100 mℓ for men and 16.7 μg/100 mℓ for women. A corresponding control group living away from the freeway had levels of 16 and 9.9 μg/100 mℓ respectively. In another study, analyses of blood samples from individuals continuously exposed to automobile exhaust during working hours (traffic policemen, taxi drivers, etc.) showed average blood lead levels of 28 μg/100 mℓ. It should be remembered that these values are average values and some people were found with levels above those quoted.

Solutions to Lead Poisoning Problems

Since the major source of lead pollution in air is automobile exhaust, an obvious solution to this problem is to get the lead out (of gasoline). Other reasons for doing this (catalytic exhaust reactor poisoning, and so forth) and the ramifications were discussed in Chapter 2.

The major sources of lead poisoning today are still old paint and industry. Solutions to these problems include education programs directed at the hazards of old paint, strict housing codes to prevent occupancy of hazardous dwellings, and better enforcement of existing safety standards directed at industry.

Suggestions for Further Reading

Journal Articles

1. Bryce-Smith, D. 1971. Lead pollution—a growing hazard to public health. *Chemistry in Britain* 7:54–56.
2. Bryce-Smith, D. 1971. Lead pollution from petrol. *Chemistry in Britain* 7:284–86.
3. Chisholm, J. J., Jr. 1971. Lead poisoning. *Scientific American* 224:15–23.
4. Craig, P. B., and Berlin, E. 1971. The air of poverty. *Environment* 13 (no. 5):2–9.
5. Hyman, M. H. 1971. Timetable for lead. *Environment* 13 (no. 5):15–23.
6. Klein, M., et al. 1970. Earthenware containers as a source of fatal lead poisoning. *The New England Journal of Medicine* 283: 669–72.
7. Mills, A. L. 1971. Lead in the environment. *Chemistry in Britain* 7:160–63.
8. Lead poisoning: risks for pencil chewers? 1971. *Science* 173: 509–10.
9. Lead poisoning: zoo animals may be the first victims. 1971. *Science* 173:130–31.

Government Documents

1. Environmental Protection Agency. 1971. *Environmental lead and public health.*

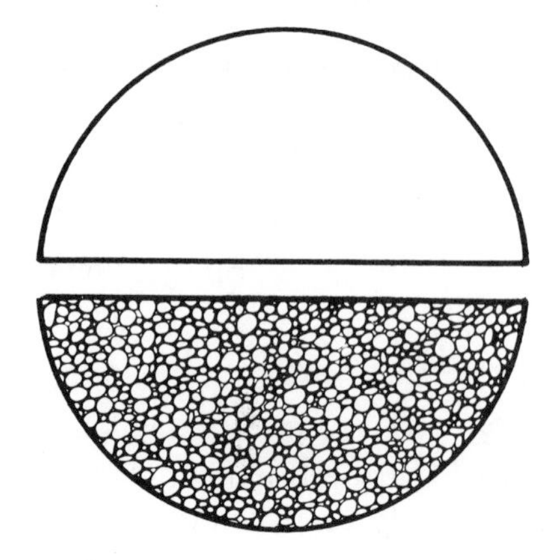

Chapter 11

Detergents

Introduction

According to a rigorous definition, a detergent is anything that behaves as a cleaning agent. This would include such materials as old-fashioned lye soap, alkaline dishwashing compounds, and solvent cleaners.

A more limited definition has come into common use, which limits detergents to those cleaning agents that include as part of their chemical makeup petrochemical or other synthetically-derived surfactants. The surfactants, to be discussed shortly, provide much of the cleaning power found in these detergents. The use of the term *detergent* in this chapter will be confined to this limited definition.

The growth in popularity of detergents during the past 20 years has been dramatic, as can be seen from Fig. 11-1. Much of this popularity is a result of their superior cleaning efficiency, particularly when used in hard water or under other unfavorable conditions.

The chemical formulation of a detergent involves numerous compounds that can be classified into three general categories: surfactant, builder, and miscellaneous.

The surfactant of a detergent functions as a wetting agent. The surface tension of water is lowered, which permits water more fully to penetrate the fabric. Also, the surfactant molecules form links between dirt particles and water. This latter activity is possible because of the "bipolar" nature of surfactant molecules. One end is nonpolar and dissolves in the dirt, while the other end is charged and is attracted to and dissolved in water.

The most commonly used surfactants are compounds known as linear alkyl sulfonates (LAS). An example of a typical member of this group is sodium dodecylbenzenesulfonate,

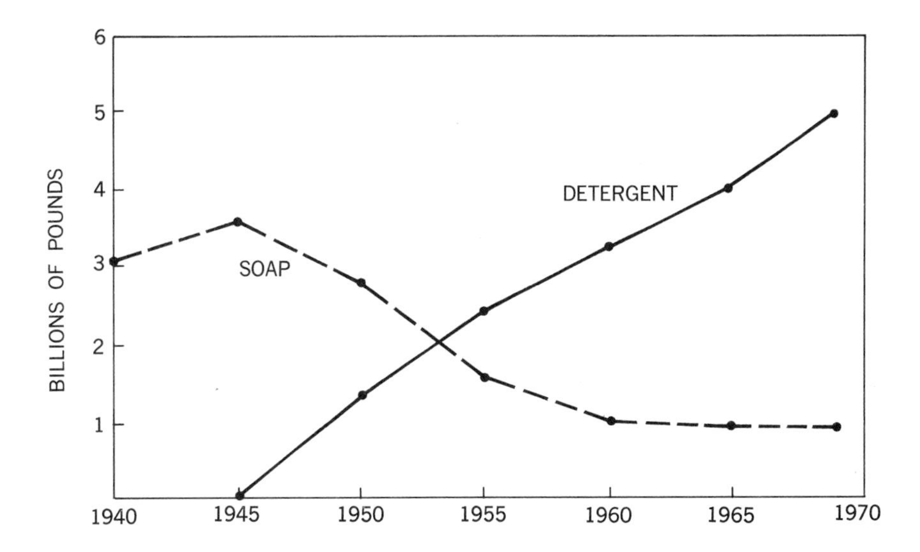

FIGURE 11-1 ESTIMATED ANNUAL SOAP AND SYNTHETIC DETERGENT SALES 1940–1970

$$CH_3{-}CH_2{-}CH_2{-}CH_2{-}CH_2{-}CH_2{-}CH_2{-}CH_2{-}CH_2{-}CH_2{-}\underset{\underset{\underset{\underset{\displaystyle ONa}{|}}{\displaystyle O{=}\overset{|}{S}{=}O}}{|}}{\displaystyle C_6H_4}}{\overset{|}{CH}}{-}CH_3$$

This form ionizes in water to give the active bipolar form

$$CH_3{-}CH_2{-}CH_2{-}CH_2{-}CH_2{-}CH_2{-}CH_2{-}CH_2{-}CH_2{-}CH_2{-}\underset{\underset{\underset{\underset{\displaystyle O^- + Na^+}{|}}{\displaystyle O{=}\overset{|}{S}{=}O}}{|}}{\displaystyle C_6H_4}}{\overset{|}{CH}}{-}CH_3$$

The main role played by the builder in a detergent is that of sequestering agent. These agents tie up hard water ions such as calcium (Ca^{+2}) or magnesium (Mg^{+2}) in the form of large water-soluble ions. In this form, the metal ions cannot interfere with the action of the surfactant. Builders also undergo a reaction (hydrolysis) with wash water which causes the water to become alkaline. This alkalinity is necessary for effective removal of dirt.

The most common builders now used are polyphosphates. An example of a popular one is sodium tripolyphosphate, $Na_5P_3O_{10}$. The active sequestering agent, the tripolyphosphate ion, has the structure

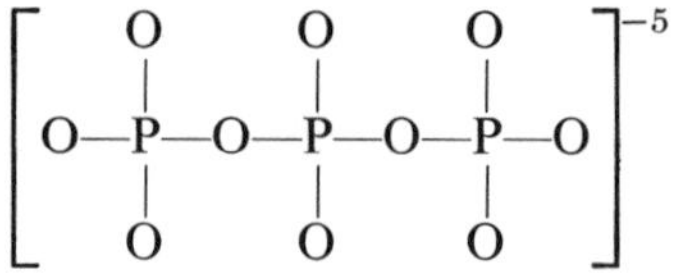

$$\left[\begin{array}{ccccccc} & O & & O & & O & \\ & | & & | & & | & \\ O- & P & -O- & P & -O- & P & -O \\ & | & & | & & | & \\ & O & & O & & O & \end{array}\right]^{-5}$$

Detergents also contain miscellaneous ingredients such as brighteners, perfumes, anti-redeposition agents and, in some products, enzymes. Brighteners are dyes which absorb invisible ultraviolet light and emit white or blue light. Anti-redeposition agents keep dirt in suspension once it has been removed from a fabric. Carboxymethylcellulose (a product of wood) is commonly used for this purpose.

Pollution Problems Involving Detergents

Water pollution problems resulting from the use of detergents involve either the surfactant or the builder. Problems involving the surfactant were the first observed, and they have largely been solved. Those involving the builder are currently the topic of much (often very emotional) concern.

Surfactants in use now are similar but not identical to those used ten years ago. The main difference is that those now in use are *biodegradable*, or readily broken down into simpler compounds by bacteria present in the environment. The nonbiodegradable types used prior to 1965 resisted bacterial action, passed through sewage treatment plants essentially unchanged, and persisted in water for long periods of time. Eventually they were decomposed, so the difference between the two is mainly the rate of decomposition.

Following World War II, detergent use increased (see Fig. 11-1) and it slowly became evident that the detergents were persisting in the environment. The evidence was not toxic water, but foam. Waste water commonly carried a huge cap of suds in areas of heavy detergent use. The foam distressed people because it was visible and esthetically unacceptable. Drinking water with a "head" on it just never caught on.

It was discovered that the surfactants used were not being degraded rapidly, which led to their buildup in waste and re-used water. The problem was solved by chemically altering the molecular structure of the compounds, making them more tantalizing to the bacteria. The change from nonbiodegradable to biodegradable surfactants was made in 1965 and apparently solved the problem.

The main builder used in detergents is $Na_5P_3O_{10}$. This material presents no biodegradability problems because the $P_3O_{10}^{-5}$ ion undergoes a slow hydrolysis reaction in the environment to produce orthophosphates that are completely nontoxic. The reaction is:

$$P_3O_{10}^{-5} + 2H_2O \rightleftharpoons 2HPO_4^{-2} + H_2PO_4^{-} \qquad \text{(eq. 11-1)}$$

Polyphosphate builders are of great concern because they and their hydrolysis products obviously contain phosphorus, which has been implicated in the eutrophication process (see Chapter 8).

In 1945, when detergent use began to increase, the potential fertilizing effect of the phosphorus included in the formulation was probably not considered important, if it was considered at all. Today it is recognized that the widespread acceptance and use of detergents places quantities of phosphorus compounds which are not negligible in waste water, and they must be considered. This is indicated dramatically by the data of Table 11-1.

TABLE 11-1 CONCENTRATION OF PHOSPHORUS IN WATER

SOURCE OF WATER	TOTAL P CONTENT (ppm)
Lake waters	0.01–0.04
Forested streams	0.02–0.10
Agricultural drainage	0.05–1.00
Domestic waste water	3.50–9.00

Adapted from *Journal of the American Water Works Association* 61:388 (1969).

It is generally accepted that detergent use accounts for about 50% of the phosphate in waste water: near large metropolitan areas where there is little dilution of waste waters, some estimates make detergents responsible for up to 70%.

Because of a rapid increase in eutrophication of natural waters (the problem is considered troublesome in 10–12% of the natural waters in the U.S.), various proposals have been made to limit the use of phosphates in or to completely remove them from detergents. Their removal from detergents has proved to be a matter of some controversy, since it is not known for sure that lowering phosphate levels in natural waters will indeed slow down the eutrophication process.

In spite of the fact that there is a great deal of conflict in scientific opinions and no proof that elimination of phosphates from laundry products will help the eutrophication problem, detergent manufacturers are taking steps to reduce the amount or to eliminate phosphates entirely from their products.

Two interesting questions are raised by this action:

1. What alternatives to phosphates exist for detergent formulations, and what problems, if any, are created by these new formulations?
2. What effects will the removal of phosphates from detergents actually have on the environmental problems of eutrophication and lake aging?

Nonphosphate Detergent Formulations

An obvious alternative to phosphate-containing detergents is soap. Soap was an acceptable cleaning agent before detergents; why not now? Two good reasons for not returning to soap are:

1. The supplies of fats and oils in the U.S. are inadequate to furnish the raw materials for the quantities of soap that would be needed. If soap were used to replace the current annual production of 5 billion pounds of detergent, about 2.3 billion pounds of tallow would be required. The use of this much tallow would put soap makers into competition for tallow that now goes into world food supplies.
2. The performance of soap in the millions of U.S.-designed washing machines is markedly poorer than detergents. These machines were specifically designed to use detergents. Soap is totally unsuitable for use in automatic dishwashers.

Detergent manufacturers are attempting to eliminate phosphates from detergents and are approaching the problem from two directions. A builder is being sought with properties similar to phosphates. An alternate solution would be the discovery of good surfactants that will work without a sequestering-type builder.

Literally thousands of compounds have been screened and tested as possible partial or full replacements for phosphate builders. A replacement has been difficult to find because of the desirable qualities possessed by phosphates.

1. Phosphates are nontoxic to aquatic life and pose no health hazard to man.
2. Phosphates are safe to use on colors, fibers, and fabrics of all types. This is especially important today with the availability and use of so many synthetics.
3. Phosphates are safe for use in washing machines, being noncorrosive and nonflammable.

Phosphates possess other good points when looked at from the standpoint of water quality.

1. They break down satisfactorily, through hydrolysis, in sewage treatment plants and surface water. After breaking down, they no longer behave as sequestering agents.
2. They do not interfere with other waste treatment procedures.
3. They can be effectively removed from waste water in treatment plants.
4. Their chemical structure and reactions are already well known, having been investigated and documented for many years.

The most promising compound to emerge from all the screening and tests is called trisodium nitrilotriacetate or NTA. Its formula is

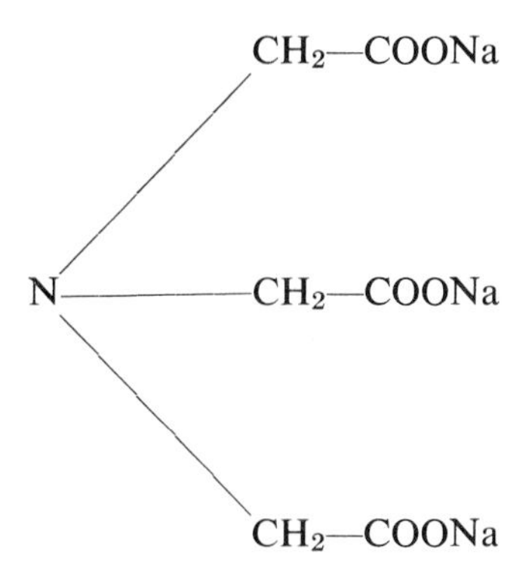

The use of this compound as a partial phosphate replacement began in early 1970. On December 18, 1970, the use of NTA came to a halt at the request of the U.S. Surgeon General, pending further studies on the substance. The Surgeon General's request was based on a report from the National Institute of Environmental Health Science (NIEHS). According to this report, NTA may have a teratogenic effect when combined with such heavy metals as cadmium or mercury. A possible result is an increased transmission of these metals across the placental barrier and into a fetus. The likelihood of birth defects is thereby increased.

Prior to its use, extensive human and environmental safety testing indicated that at the levels used currently and contemplated for the near future, NTA was safe. Normally, NTA is degraded in waste treatment systems and in the environment. In the degraded state, it loses all ability to combine with metals. It does not, however, degrade under anaerobic conditions such as may be found in some septic tanks. This raised the possibility that such nondegraded NTA might react with heavy metals known to be present in water.

This situation indicates the great care that must be taken to insure that alternatives to phosphate do not present equal or greater hazards to the environment. One big concern relative to phosphate replacements is that their chemistry and behavior in the environment will not be known and will have to be obtained over long periods of time by careful observation and experience.

As matters now stand, NTA is not available for use as a phosphate substitute. Only further scientific study will tell whether the situation is temporary or permanent. Even if NTA is subsequently proved safe, perhaps the wide publicity given to the initial findings will have created attitudes in the consumer's mind which will prevent popular acceptance of NTA as a component of detergents.

On the basis of consumer reports, detergent manufacturers are of the opinion that if the phosphate content of detergents is lowered without proper replacement, most people will simply use more detergent in order to achieve results that satisfy their own standards. The net result would be about the same amount of phosphate in sewage, but at a higher cost to consumers.

The quest for useful combinations of surfactants and nonsequestering type builders has been moderately successful, and some nonphosphate detergents of this type are on the market. The surfactants are combined with builders that markedly increase alkalinity and which precipitate hard water ions, rather than sequester them. Typically, carbonates and silicates are the builders used.

These builders have some disadvantages. The buildup of calcium and magnesium salt residues is one. These solids can become deposited in the articles to be washed, with the result that the wash looks "dull." Sequestering builders keep the metals in solution as large ions and avoid this problem. The precipitating builders give much more alkalinity to the wash water than do phosphates. Phosphate detergents produce wash water with a *p*H of 9–10.5. The nonphosphate detergents usually result in wash water with a *p*H of 10.5–11. A solution with a *p*H of 11 and above is approaching a value where skin corrosion, serious eye irritation, and ingested toxicity become problems. At these high *p*H values the solutions apparently form gels with protein tissues and become very difficult to remove before serious damage has been done. The FDA is beginning to screen nonphosphate detergents for such excessive *p*H problems.

Research is in progress following both approaches to the problem despite the fact that nearly everyone agrees that reformulation of detergents is really a short-range objective. The best long-range method for controlling all plant nutrients, including phosphates, is advanced sewage treatment systems. Phosphates can now be removed by such treatment, and methods are being developed to remove other plant nutrients.

Detergent reformulation may have to suffice for a while because of the time lag in getting public financing for comprehensive treatment systems. Clothes might not be whiter than white in the near future, but simply clean.

Effects of Phosphate Removal on the Environment

After all the previous information of this chapter has been weighed, one question still remains: will the removal of phosphates from detergents help solve the environmental problem of eutrophication? The answer, unfortunately, is not an unqualified yes. In fact, some scientists feel that such removal will have very little effect on the eutrophication problem. In order to illustrate the difficulty involved in making such a decision, some arguments of those in favor of removing phosphates from detergents and those against such action will be given.

The arguments of both sides are based on the "limiting reactant" principle, which says that the growth of algae is limited by the nutrient in shortest supply relative to the amount needed. As soon as this element is exhausted, growth stops. Research indicates that any of the elements carbon, nitrogen, or phosphorus may be limiting, depending on water conditions.

The arguments against removing phosphates from detergents are given first since they are in favor of leaving things as they are:

1. Studies in nutrient-rich lakes indicate an excess of phosphorus. This implies phosphorus is not the limiting factor in these instances, although it may be in nutrient-poor lakes.
2. Carbon makes up nearly 50% of the weight of algae. All this carbon is assimilated through photosynthesis of CO_2. Until recently, few investigators have questioned the sources of this essential nutrient which is needed in huge amounts. Land plants have large leaves in contact with air, their source of CO_2. Water plants must draw most CO_2 from the water, so the amount of dissolved CO_2 may be the limiting factor rather than phosphorus.
3. Phosphates, after once being introduced into a body of water, are continually recycled in the green plants and algae. When the plants and algae die, the phosphates are released and used again by other plants. This regeneration of phosphorus occurs much more rapidly than that of nitrogen.
4. Large amounts of phosphorus are stored in the bottom muds of lakes in the form of slightly soluble salts of calcium, magnesium and iron. Recent research has shown this phosphorus to be in equilibrium with dissolved phosphorus compounds. So even if phosphates were removed from incoming water, the bottom muds would provide a supply for many years. This relationship is shown in Fig. 11-2 (see following page) which also shows the factors that influence the equilibrium.
5. Problems could arise involving the substitutes for phosphates if they are organic sequestering agents. They do not react with water as phosphate does, and so they retain sequestering properties until degraded. Remember the NTA problem. Also, since they presumably will be biodegradable they will require oxygen and increase BOD problems. The degradation products will be compounds of carbon and possibly nitrogen, both of which are plant nutrients and could cause problems.

The arguments in favor of removing phosphates are:

1. Even though some water may contain phosphorus in excess, the technology for its control is further advanced than that for either carbon or nitrogen. If phosphate were removed it could be made the limiting factor and thus control the growth of algae.
2. The sources of phosphorus are well known, and they are not as varied as those of carbon or nitrogen. This makes control easier. For example, approximately 70% of the phosphorus entering Lake Erie, one of the most polluted lakes, comes from point (localized) sources that are partially controllable. Only about 40% of the nitrogen entering the lake is from similar sources.
3. Carbon and nitrogen are readily available to aquatic plants from atmospheric sources if they are not present in the water. There is no common

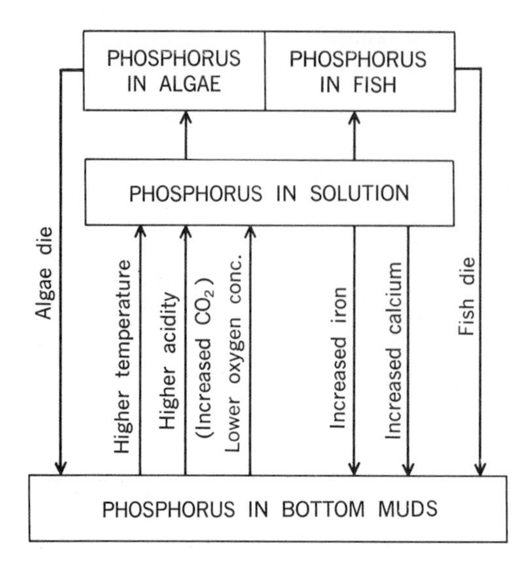

FIGURE 11-2 FACTORS AFFECTING PHOSPHORUS EQUILIBRIA

Redrawn from U.S. Senate Subcommittee on Air and Water Pollution, *Water Pollution—1970*, part 4, p. 1507.

atmospheric source for phosphorus. Carbon comes from dissolved CO_2 of the air. Nitrogen is also dissolved in the water from air and then converted to usable forms by certain aquatic plants, including the blue-green algae.

In summary, it can be seen that those against removing phosphates from detergents are not convinced that phosphorus is the limiting factor. Furthermore, they feel that if it is, eliminating it from detergents will not solve the eutrophication problem because a large source of phosphorus is present in the bottom mud. They also seem to feel that in light of the previous two arguments, it is not worth the risk of introducing new problems in the form of a phosphate substitute.

Those favoring phosphorus removal, on the other hand, feel that because phosphorus is the most easily controlled of the plant nutrients, it should be eliminated from detergents and made the limiting factor even if it is not the limiting factor at present. They also feel that the storehouse of phosphorus contained in bottom mud must be used up eventually. Why not start using it up immediately? Both sides agree that the best long-range plan is to treat all waste waters and remove excess plant nutrients.

Suggestions for Further Reading

Journal Articles

1. Brenner, T. E. 1969. Biodegradable detergents and water pollution. In *Advances in Environmental Sciences*, vol. 1, ed. Pitts, J. N., and Metcalf, R. L., pp. 147–96. New York: Wiley-Interscience.
2. Hammond, A. L. 1971. Phosphate replacements: problems with the washday miracle. *Science* 172:361–63.
3. Weiss, C. M. 1969. Relationship of phosphates to eutrophication. *Journal of the American Water Works Association.* 61:387–91.

Government Documents

1. FMC Corporation. 1970. The eutrophication problem: a review and critical analysis. In *Water pollution—1970.* Hearings before the Committee on Public Works, U.S. Senate, 91st Congress, 2nd session, pp. 1478–1520.
2. U.S. Dept. of Commerce. 1971. *Detergents—a status report.* Sub-Council Report, National Industrial Pollution Control Council.
3. U.S. Dept. of Commerce. 1970. *Detergents.* Sub-Council Report, National Industrial Pollution Control Council.

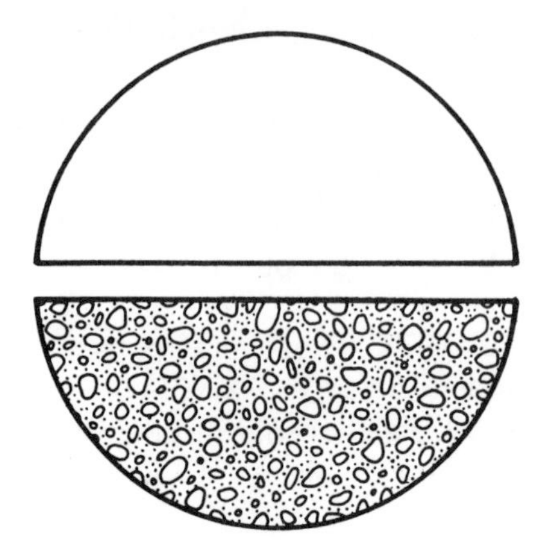

Chapter 12

Synthetic Organic Insecticides

Introduction

Man finds it necessary to do battle with natural "pests," including insects, because they compete with him for his means of survival. When pests threaten, man tries to find a means for destroying them.

According to the latest estimates, 3 million different species of insects are now in existence. This is far more than the number of all other animal and plant species combined. The number of individual insects alive at any one time is thought to be about 1 billion billion (10^{18}). Of this vast number, 99.9% are, from the human point of view, either harmless or, in fact, helpful. A few, such as pollen-transferring bees, are considered indispensible. The troublesome species comprise 0.1% of the total, or about 3000 species. Most of these are agricultural pests or carriers of human and animal diseases.

If man is to have food, remain relatively disease-free, and prosper, the freedom of these selected few insects to pursue their natural activities must be destroyed. At our present stage of technological development, synthetic organic chemical insecticides are the most significant means of accomplishing this task.

These insecticides have come under intense scrutiny as a result of the increasing attention given to the relationships between man-made chemicals and the environment. The resulting investigations indicate that not all properties of some insecticides are compatible with the environment. It is the purpose of this chapter to investigate some of the chemistry and chemical problems related to insecticides and their use.

Classes and Properties of Synthetic Organic Insecticides

Synthetic organic insecticides can be placed into three classes, based on molecular structure and composition. These classes are:

1. Organochlorine insecticides
2. Organophosphorus insecticides
3. Carbamate insecticides

The amount of each one in use decreases in the order listed. Examples of each class and their basic structures are given in Table 12-1.

TABLE 12-1 CLASSES OF SYNTHETIC ORGANIC INSECTICIDES

CLASS	BASIC CORE STRUCTURAL UNIT	EXAMPLES OF INSECTICIDES
Organochlorine	Cl—C— (three further bonds) Three bonds form, as indicated, in various ways with other molecular fragments to form whole molecules.	DDT Methoxychlor Aldrin Dieldrin

TABLE 12-1 (Continued)

CLASS	BASIC CORE STRUCTURAL UNIT	EXAMPLES OF INSECTICIDES
Organophosphorus	$(-O)_2P(=S)-O-$ There are slight variations in the position of S and O from compound to compound.	$(CH_3CH_2O)_2P(=S)-O-C_6H_4-NO_2$ Parathion
		$(CH_3O)_2P(=S)-S-CH(-C(=O)-O-CH_2CH_3)-CH_2-C(=O)-O-CH_2CH_3$ Malathion
Carbamate	$>N-C(=O)-O-$	$H(CH_3)N-C(=O)-O-C_{10}H_7$ Carbaryl (Sevin)
		$H(CH_3)N-C(=O)-O-C_6H_4-O-C(H)(CH_3)-CH_3$ Baygon

As might be expected, the properties of the compounds vary between classes, and there is also wide variation within each class, depending upon the groups attached to the basic core structure. Two very important properties, especially when environmental effects are considered, are toxicity and ease of degradation.

Toxicity

The toxicity varies within each class and between classes. It cannot be said that one class is absolutely more toxic than another. The relative toxicities of most of the compounds of Table 12-1 are given in Table 12-2. These toxicities are expressed in 50% lethal dose values (LD_{50}). This term represents the quantity of insecticide which, when administered in a single dose, is lethal to 50% of a group of test animals. The value is usually given as milligrams of insecticide given per kilogram of animal body weight (mg/kg or ppm).

TABLE 12-2 RELATIVE INSECTICIDE TOXICITIES

INSECTICIDE	CLASS	ORAL LD_{50} VALUE mg/kg or ppm
DDT	Organochlorine	113
Methoxychlor	Organochlorine	6000
Aldrin	Organochlorine	39
Dieldrin	Organochlorine	46
Parathion	Organophosphorus	3.6
Malathion	Organophosphorus	1000
Carbaryl	Carbamate	540

Data selected from U.S. Dept. of Health, Education, and Welfare, *Report of the Secretary's Commission on Pesticides and Their Relationship to Environmental Health*, pp. 312–13.

The data of Table 12-2 are for animal tests and, of course, similar data are not available for humans. However, an extrapolation to human populations is possible in a general way, for it is usually true that insecticides highly toxic to experimental animals are highly toxic to man. This generalization is based primarily on inadvertent human experiments. Accidental contamination of food products (usually wheat and flour) has resulted in some epidemics of insecticide poisoning. Accidental parathion contamination of this type caused 102 deaths in India during 1958, and 88 deaths in Colombia during 1967.

Biochemical research has provided some evidence concerning the actual mechanisms by which these materials cause death. The autonomic (involuntary) nervous system is affected, resulting in tremors, convulsions, and eventual death for insects, birds, and mammals.

The site of toxic activity for organophosphorus and carbamate insecticides is the synaptic gap of nerves. A nerve impulse moves along a nerve fiber electrically until this tiny gap is reached. The impulse triggers the release of a molecule of the compound acetylcholine, which quickly diffuses across the gap (a distance of 2–5 millionths of an inch) and is accepted by another nerve fiber. The molecule of acetylcholine triggers an electrical impulse which travels along the second fiber. The acetylcholine molecule will continue to send impulses down the second fiber until it is chemically changed. An enzyme is present at the receptor site which quickly changes acetylcholine into a nonactive molecule before more than one impulse can be triggered. This enzyme, acetylcholinesterase (ACHE) is attacked and deactivated by organophosphorus and carbamate insecticides. With the means for its deactivation removed, acetylcholine triggers impulse after impulse down receptor nerve fibers. This causes tremors in the involuntary muscle system, convulsions, and death.

The mechanism by which organochlorine molecules operate toxically is not as well understood. It is thought that they dissolve in the fatty membrane surrounding nerve fibers, and there interfere with the vital transport of ions in and out of the fiber. This latter process is involved in the transmission of electrical impulses along the fiber. Again, the effects are tremors and convulsions.

Degradation or Chemical Breakdown

The majority of insecticide molecules placed into the environment are not consumed by the pests they are meant to destroy. A question of vital importance is: What happens to that majority of molecules not consumed by the pests? How rapidly do they break down or degrade in the environment? The chemical structure of the insecticide is the major factor involved in the rate of degradation. Insecticides of the same class with similar structures will behave similarly, but not identically, to one another during degradation.

Organophosphorus and carbamate compounds usually degrade quite rapidly into simpler substances. Organochlorine compounds generally persist unchanged in the environment for longer periods of time. Half-life data, illustrating the relative degradation times involved, are given in Table 12-3 for the 3 classes. Values for specific members of any class may fall outside the ranges given in Table 12-3, but the general times involved are as indicated.

TABLE 12-3 PERSISTENCE OF INSECTICIDES IN SOIL

CLASS OF INSECTICIDE	HALF-LIFE, $t_{\frac{1}{2}}$ (YEARS)
Carbamate	approx. 0.02 (1 week)
Organophosphorus	approx. 0.02–0.2 (1–10 weeks)
Organochlorine	approx. 2–4

Data selected from J. N. Pitts and R. L. Metcalf, eds., *Advances in Environmental Science*, Vol. 1, p. 15 (New York: Wiley-Interscience, 1969).

It should be emphasized that even though chemical structure is the major factor involved, environmental conditions may also influence degradation times. Examples of these other conditions are: soil type, amount of organic matter present, temperature, and extent of cultivation. Thus the values of Table 12-3 are really broad guidelines concerning stabilities of insecticides. However, an important fact illustrated by the data of the table is that degradation of the first two classes takes only weeks, but years may pass before organochlorine compounds are degraded.

The complete chemistry involved in the degradation of insecticides is not known. Organophosphorus and carbamate compounds degrade by means of hydrolysis (reaction with water) reactions to give essentially nontoxic products. Organochlorine molecules do not hydrolyze but must be broken down by slow microbial degradation. Because the reaction is so slow, much of the material is volatilized or leached from the soil before degradation is completed. Another important difference is that the degradation products are usually toxic and persistent in the environment.

DDT—A Controversial Compound

In order to illustrate the benefits obtained, problems encountered, and chemistry involved when pesticides are used, a detailed discussion of DDT will be presented. DDT is chosen because it is the most commonly used and most widely studied insecticide.

The story of this well-known substance is one of rags to riches to rags. The compound has been in the news almost continuously since the late 1940s when it was first widely used as an insecticide. Twenty years ago, all comments about DDT were of a positive nature. It was a relatively new compound, and the short-term effects of its use against agricultural and health pests were truly spectacular. Today, most statements concerning DDT are negative. The change has taken place because of recent discoveries of the nature of its long-term effects on the environment, some of which are very detrimental.

It should be remembered that, although the following discussion deals only with DDT, other insecticides have similar properties and some have similar long-term effects. Thus, much of the discussion may be applied to insecticides in general.

History and Beneficial Effects of DDT

In 1874, Othmar Zeidler, a German chemist, synthesized the compound dichlorodiphenyltrichloroethane (DDT) as part of his doctoral research. The compound was not particularly unusual, having been synthesized by simple substitutions on the common ethane molecule.

```
   H  H                          Cl H                            Cl H
   |  |      remove 3 H's        |  |       remove 2 H's         |  |
H—C—C—H  ——————————————→  Cl—C—C—H  ——————————————→  Cl—C—C—C6H4—Cl
   |  |      & replace with      |  |       & replace with       |  |
   H  H      Cl's                Cl H       C6H5—Cl              Cl C6H4
                                                                     |
                                                                     Cl
Ethane                                                           DDT
```

He published his work as a short note in a journal and the compound lay forgotten for many years.

Sixty-five years later, this same compound was "rediscovered" by a Swiss entomologist, Paul Mueller, who was studying the usefulness of various compounds as insecticides. He found Zeidler's compound to be extremely toxic to insects. The Swiss firm for which he worked began immediately to manufacture the substance. In 1942, this firm delivered 6 pounds of the compound to the U.S. for testing.

The onset of World War II had deprived the U.S. of its supplier of pyrethrum, a louse control agent, and the military quickly found the new compound useful as a delousing agent. Other successful applications of the new insecticide followed rapidly. DDT was heralded for its success in halting a typhus epidemic in Italy during 1943–44. As a result of the use of DDT, World War II was the first war to claim more dead by combat wounds than by insect-spread communicable diseases.

After the war, DDT was effectively used to combat the insect carriers of malaria, yellow fever, and typhus. Millions of houses and people were dusted and sprayed with the compound in all-out campaigns against fleas, houseflies, and mosquitoes. Literally millions of lives were saved by the material. Statistics show that DDT campaigns in Ceylon reduced human mortality by 34% in a single year. Such crop pests as the cotton boll worm were brought under control. The increased crop yields provided economic benefits for the farmer.

In 1948 Paul Mueller was awarded the Nobel Prize in chemistry for his discovery of the insecticidal properties of DDT. The compound was at the zenith of its popularity.

Problems with DDT

Because of the tremendous success of DDT in controlling pests, its use in large quantities was continued through the 1950s and into the early 1960s. Annual production figures for DDT are given in Table 12-4. This large scale use led to two problems that only slowly became apparent and eventually led to a decrease in use of DDT.

1. Certain insects developed a resistance or immunity to the compound.

TABLE 12-4 PRODUCTION OF DDT IN UNITS OF 10^3 METRIC TONS/YEAR (UNITED STATES ONLY)

YEAR	DDT	YEAR	DDT
1944	4.4	1957	56.6
1945	15.1	1958	66.0
1946	20.7	1959	71.2
1947	22.5	1960	74.6
1948	9.2	1961	77.9
1949	17.2	1962	75.9
1950	35.5	1963	81.3
1951	48.2	1964	56.2
1952	45.4	1965	64.0
1953	38.4	1966	64.2
1954	44.2	1967	47.0
1955	59.0	1968	63.4
1956	62.6	Total	1,220.0

Redrawn from *Man's Impact on the Global Environment*, p. 132 (Report of the Study of Critical Environmental Problems [Cambridge, Mass.: The MIT Press, 1970]).

2. Natural processes were found to spread DDT from target areas to non-target areas and ultimately throughout the environment.

As early as 1947, Italian researchers reported that the housefly was becoming immune to the compound. Other researchers reported similar findings from many locations in the world. Apparently the attempts to completely eliminate certain insects led to the death of the vast majority. The few remaining, however, were evidently immune to DDT. These naturally immune specimens were now reproducing and developing resistant strains. By 1948, 12 species were found to be immune; by 1954, 25; by 1957, 76; by 1960, 137; and by 1967, 165. This acquired immunity was the motivation behind the development of many new insecticides.

The movement of DDT throughout the environment occurs because DDT is a persistent pesticide that remains chemically unchanged in the environment for long periods of time. Pesticides of this type show an advantage over non-persistent types by remaining effective over long periods of time and requiring fewer applications. An obvious disadvantage is that the longer persistance increases the chances that DDT will move out of treated areas and damage non-target organisms. Today, DDT residues are found throughout the environment and in many living organisms. The accumulation of DDT in the marine environment is of particular concern. This accumulation and its effects on species such as fish and birds of prey are discussed later in this chapter.

Evaluation of DDT Effects

The determination of DDT effects on non-target organisms is not a simple process because of the many variables at work in nature. Imagine, for example, that the population of a certain species of wildlife is declining in a particular geographic area. Numerous questions must be answered to uncover the causes of the decline. Several typical questions are:

1. Is the species dying or is the decline caused by unnatural migration?
2. If migration is the answer, what is causing the migration?
3. If the species is dying, are pesticides or other factors at fault?
4. If pesticides are at fault, how were they transported to the non-target species?
5. Again, if pesticides are involved, what physiological effect does the killing and what pesticide dosage is required?

Answers to these and other similar questions are nearly impossible to find, when natural populations are involved, because of difficulties encountered in trying to single out each factor and determine its contribution to the over-all problem.

The declining numbers of some kinds of birds of prey is an example of the problems encountered when dealing with natural populations. Some wildlife biologists suspected that DDT residues were contributing to the decline but they could not be sure that other factors such as the urbanization of the birds' natural habitat were not involved. Birds were reared in the laboratory, and fed measured doses of pesticides in concentrations similar to those present in the natural habitat. Only after these experiments could the pesticides be identified as the agents causing the observed effects. Much of the evidence quoted in the following discussions was gathered from similar laboratory experiments concerning the effects of DDT.

Effects of DDT in the Marine Environment

A 1971 report of the National Research Council of the National Academy of Sciences contained an estimate that the oceans are the ultimate accumulation site for as much as 25% of all DDT used to date. This accumulation results because DDT very easily reaches ponds, lakes, and rivers in a variety of ways, including the following:

1. DDT may be applied directly to water in the form of aerial sprays to control water-borne insects.
2. DDT may accidentally fall on water when it is sprayed from airplanes to control forest or agricultural pests.
3. DDT may be carried down from the atmosphere in rain. Rainwater samples have been found that contained up to 0.34 ppb DDT.
4. DDT residues may reach water in surface runoff from soil. The pesticide is relatively insoluble in water but it strongly adsorbs to organic matter like that present in many soils. When streams or rivers become contaminated with relatively high levels of DDT it is usually through wind or water erosion of treated soil.

Even though large amounts of DDT have reached the waterways, and ultimately the oceans, the actual concentration in the oceans is quite low because of the dilution effect exerted by the huge volume of ocean water involved. Concentrations of DDT in the parts per billion range for fresh water and parts per trillion for ocean water are typical.

Why is there such great concern about DDT in the marine environments if concentrations are so low? Much of the concern is generated by the ability of many plants and animals to concentrate DDT (and other similar pesticides) in their body tissues. Oysters and water fleas are extreme examples of organisms with this ability.

Oysters are able to concentrate DDT from levels of 1 ppb in seawater to levels of 700 ppm in their bodies. The body concentration is 70,000 times as large as the seawater concentration. Water fleas are even more efficient and can concentrate DDT levels of 0.5 ppb in seawater by a factor of 100,000 times.

Normally, the capacity for biological concentration is not as great as this. However, when the process is repeated through several links in a food chain,

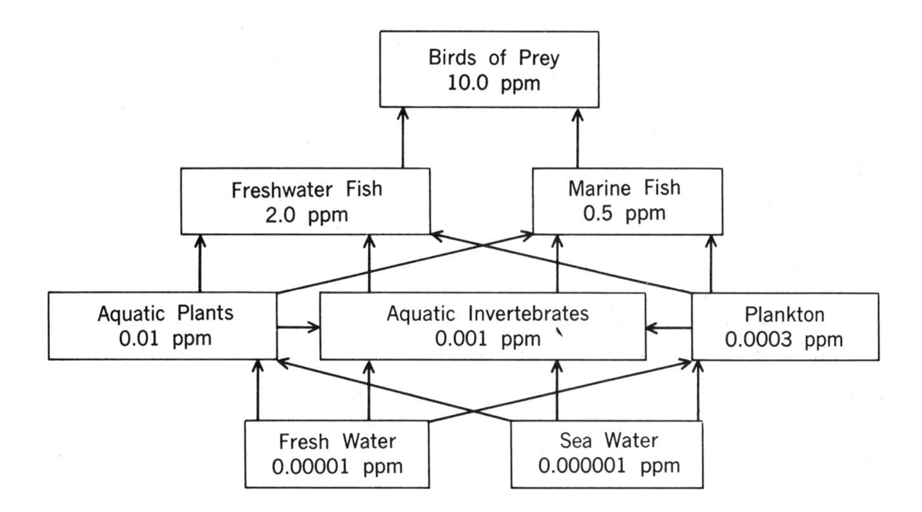

FIGURE 12-1 A TYPICAL FOOD-CHAIN CONCENTRATION OF DDT

Redrawn, with permission, from part of a chart in Clive A. Edwards, *Persistent Pesticides in the Environment* (Cleveland: CRC Press, 1971), p. v.

extremely high concentrations of DDT residues can result in species at the top of the food chain. Typical values for a food chain concentration pattern are given in Fig. 12-1.

Laboratory and field studies of fish point out some of the possible problems that exist and are related directly and indirectly to the presence of DDT in marine and other aquatic environments.

1. DDT can induce behavioral changes in fish that could lead to reproduction problems. New Brunswick salmon from a DDT-sprayed region were found to be unusually sensitive to low temperatures and, as a result, chose to populate waters of higher temperature than their normal habitat. If this occurred in nature, salmon might lay their eggs in regions where the young could not survive. A similar result was found in mosquito fish. After exposure to low DDT levels of 0.1 to 20 ppb for 24 hours, mosquito fish showed a definite preference for waters of higher salinity than did unexposed fish.

2. DDT in fish eggs affects the mortality rate of the young. DDT tends to concentrate in the fatty tissues of fish. The ovaries contain such tissues and the concentration of DDT in these organs can lead to high concentrations in eggs. In the speckled sea trout, found on the south Texas coast, DDT residues in ripe eggs are at a level of about 8 ppm. This level is higher than the 5 ppm level found to cause 100% failure in the development of young fresh-water trout. Sea trout inventories in one Texas area have decreased from 30 fish per acre in 1964 to 0.2 fish per acre in 1969. This constitutes presumptive evidence of reproductive failure.

Lower DDT levels may also be injurious. It has been found that when levels of DDT and its metabolites are higher than 0.4 ppm in the eggs of hatchery trout, the mortality rate in the resulting young ranged from 30% to 90% in the 60-day period following hatching.

3. DDT may be directly toxic to certain species of fish (especially the young) and cause large fish kills. The LC_{50} value (concentration of DDT in the water which kills 50% of the test fish) for various common fish is in the range of 1–10 ppb. Typical LC_{50} values for a 96-hour exposure are: Coho salmon—4 ppb; rainbow trout—7 ppb; and yellow perch—9 ppb.

4. DDT may accumulate in the body tissues of commercial fish to an extent that human consumption of the fish is possibly dangerous. During the spring of 1969, wide publicity was given to the fact that Coho salmon, obtained from Lake Michigan and destined for commercial sale, were seized by the FDA because of high DDT content. The fish contained DDT at concentrations in the 10–20 ppm range. As a result, the FDA established a maximum level of 5 ppm in fish used for human consumption.

The average concentration of DDT in a few selected species of fish caught in the Great Lakes during 1970 are given in Table 12-5.

TABLE 12-5 AVERAGE CONCENTRATIONS OF DDT IN A FEW SELECTED FISH SPECIES FROM THE GREAT LAKES

LAKE	FISH SPECIES	DDT (ppm)
Michigan	Lake trout	6.96
	Yellow perch	3.22
Ontario	American smelt	1.58
	Yellow perch	2.10
Huron	American smelt	0.75
	Yellow perch	1.59
Erie	Walleye	1.12
	Yellow perch	0.87
Superior	Coho salmon	1.02
	Lake trout	7.44

Redrawn from Executive Office of the President—Office of Science and Technology, *Ecological Effects of Pesticides on Non-Target Species* (1971), p. 169.

Effects of DDT on Birds

It is now clear that residues of DDT occur in the tissues and eggs of many species of birds found both in Europe and North America. The process of biological concentration repeated through several links in the food chain appears to be occurring here as it does in fish. Those species with highest DDT concentrations are the fish-eating birds followed in order by flesh eaters, flesh and plant eaters, and plant eaters. Figure 12-2 shows the variation of DDT levels among various species. The dependence of DDT concentration on diet is evident.

The accumulation of lethal levels of DDT through food consumption is

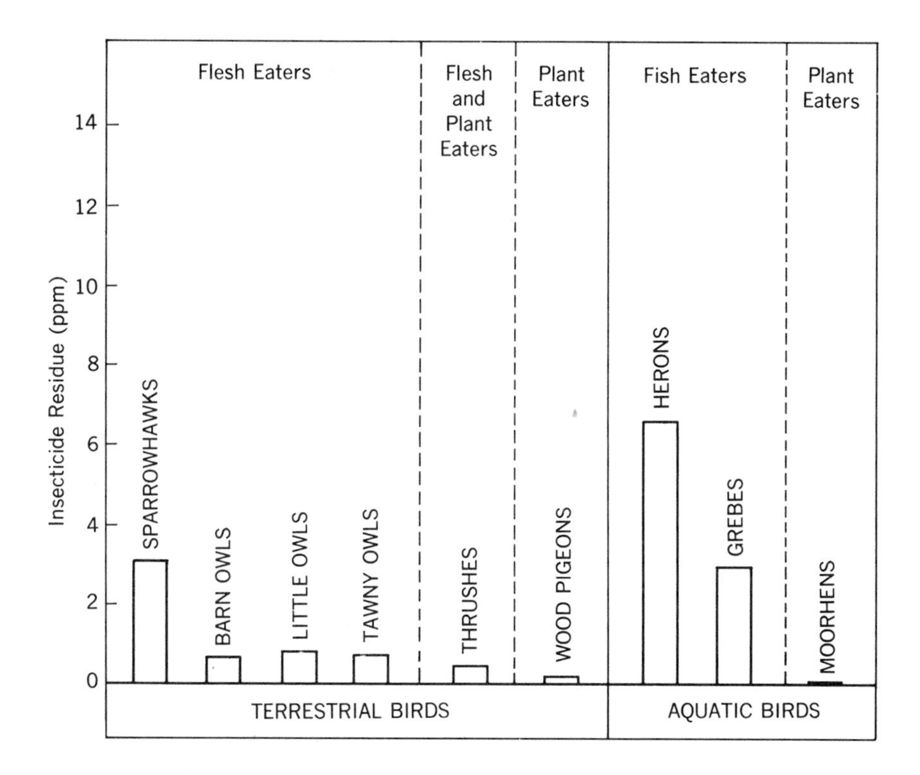

FIGURE 12-2 AVERAGE CONCENTRATION OF DDT RESIDUE IN THE BREAST MUSCLE OF DIFFERENT TYPES OF BIRDS

Redrawn from Executive Office of the President—Office of Science and Technology, *Ecological Effects of Pesticides on Non-target Species*, p. 165.

known to take place in birds inhabiting areas where DDT use is great. The application of DDT on elm trees for the control of Dutch elm disease has resulted in a high mortality rate for robins and other birds. Some of the sprayed DDT apparently drips to the ground and concentrates in the soil. Soil concentrations may reach levels as high as 18 ppm. This DDT is ingested, along with soil, by earthworms which in turn are eaten by robins and other birds.

In a 1965 study conducted in environments containing DDT-treated elms, pesticide residues were found at a 9.9 ppm level in soil. This concentration increased to 141 ppm in earthworms and to 444 ppm in the brains of adult robins. In another study conducted on dying robins collected from a DDT-treated area, the median residue of DDT in the birds' bodies was 3 mg. Calculations indicate that the ingestion of fewer than 100 earthworms would cause a robin to accumulate the lethal 3 mg dosage.

Sub-lethal dosages of DDT have been reported to cause significant changes in the physiology of some species of birds. A correlation has been found between the amount of DDT residues in eggs and the egg-shell thickness of a number of birds of prey. This is thought to occur as a result of DDT inhibition of an enzyme that controls calcium metabolism in the birds. Less calcium is deposited in the egg shells and the resulting fragile eggs are less able to withstand the rigors of incubation. This results in a large amount of reproductive failure. In a laboratory study, American sparrow hawks were fed a diet for two years that contained DDT residues at environmental concentrations. The hawks showed an average 10% decrease in egg-shell thickness.

Other pesticide effects on reproduction are known besides egg-shell thinning. A study of finches found the ovulation time doubled when the birds were fed DDT along with their normal diet. This, of course, caused an increase in the time required for a new generation to be produced.

DDT in Humans

Man stands at the top of every food chain in which he is involved, and accumulation of DDT should therefore occur. The information contained in Table 12-6 indicates this to be the case.

TABLE 12-6 DDT CONCENTRATIONS IN MAN

LOCATION	DDT CONCENTRATION (ppm)
U.S. (average)	11.0
Alaska (Eskimo)	2.8
England	2.2
West Germany	2.3
France	5.2
Canada	5.3
Hungary	12.4
Israel	19.2
India	12.8–31.0

Data selected from a more extensive table in George M. Woodwell, "Toxic Substances and Ecological Cycles," *Scientific American* 216:31 (1967).

It is believed that the main source of DDT in man is food, although home use and dust-laden air have been implicated as well.

The available evidence concerning the effects of current human DDT levels is limited. Much that is known is the result of case studies of accidental poisonings. A detailed survey of such incidents reveals that the general effect on man is that discussed before, increased excitability of the nervous system.

It appears that present levels of exposure to DDT among the general population have not produced any observable adverse effect when used in controlled studies conducted on volunteers.

In spite of the lack of evidence concerning adverse effects on humans, it is obvious that DDT is very suspect at this time. Its effects on the environment seem irrefutable. The compound has now completed the rags to riches to rags story.

At the present time, a total ban on DDT use is being considered. Limitations on its use are in effect in the U.S. and some other countries. The complete ban is a matter of controversy much like the situation with detergent phosphates (see Chapter 11). Those against a complete ban have presented the following arguments and proposals:

1. No human has yet been seriously injured as a consequence of normal DDT use.
2. The effects on birds and fish appear to reflect results of heavy overdoses rather than proper use. There is little doubt that this has occurred. Aerial spraying and annual "insurance" treatment of large areas (whether pests were present or not) have contributed significantly to the amount of residues present in the environment.
3. The establishment of a corps of specialists trained in the proper use of DDT could minimize its disadvantages. Only these specially trained individuals would be licensed to use the material and would know where it could be legally used and in what maximum dosages.
4. If DDT is totally banned, other more costly chemical pesticides must be used in its place since alternate control methods are not yet available (see the next section of this chapter). Many of the known substitutes degrade more rapidly but are much more toxic. Parathion, for example, is 30 times more toxic than DDT and accidental poisonings with this material have already taken place.
5. It is not in the best interests of world-wide health to confront readers of newspapers and magazines in India, for example, with headlined articles about total DDT bans in affluent countries. This could cause groundless anxieties about the substance being used selectively to alleviate desperately serious health problems in backward countries. Such programs definitely require an insecticide that is cheap, persistent, effective, and safe to those contacting it under proper conditions. DDT is an insecticide with these characteristics.

Those in favor of the ban say:

1. The effects of DDT on humans are not known and it is better to be safe than sorry.
2. Birds and some fish are experiencing reproductive failure and direct poisoning as a result of DDT in the environment.
3. Many new pesticides, although more toxic, degrade faster than DDT and so do not persist in the environment.

Both sides agree that the best solution to the problem is the development of alternatives to DDT-like chemical insecticides. This will probably require an appreciable amount of time.

Alternatives to DDT-like Chemical Pesticides

The harmful effects of DDT on the environment can be expected in some degree for other similar chemical compounds. Because of these problems, interest has been growing in devising alternate pest control methods. These alternatives are in various stages of development and some require more basic research before their worth can be evaluated. Some possible alternatives are:

1. *Use of biological controls.* This approach involves the use of natural predators, parasites, and pathogens (disease-causing organisms) to destroy insects. The potential value of such controls appears promising since such organisms, particularly pathogens, are very specific toward their hosts and remain inactive against others. The principal hazard of this approach is the possibility that predators introduced to control pests might themselves become a problem.
2. *Development of resistant varieties of plants.* Agricultural researchers have succeeded in developing varieties of plants that are resistant to specific insects and diseases. Such plants, once developed, represent a safe, cheap, and practical method for overcoming insect pests. The use of resistant plants has two main drawbacks. Usually, many years are required to develop a commercially acceptable plant. After plants are produced, new strains of insects or plant pathogens sometimes develop to which the "resistant" plants are no longer resistant.
3. *Use of attractants.* In their search for food, insects respond to various chemical substances in plants. They also respond to chemical sex attractants produced by other members of their species. Light and sound are also known to attract some types of insects. Attractants are being used to lure insects into traps where they can be killed. Considerable effort is being devoted to the tasks of isolating, determining the structure of, and synthesizing attractants in order to obtain quantities large enough to be tested as possible control agents for several major insect pests.
4. *Genetic control.* In this approach, sexually sterile insects are released to mate with normal insects. The native population of insects is first reduced using other methods. While this is being done, insects are reared in the laboratory and the males are sterilized by radiation or the use of sterilizing chemicals. The sterilized males are then released into an infested area. The number of sterile males released is planned to be much greater than the number of normal males in the natural population. As the release of sterile males is done periodically and with each succeeding generation, fewer and fewer productive matings take place. Eventually the insect population is reduced to zero.
5. *Bioenvironmental control.* Certain common practices or procedures can be changed in a way that adversely affects insect pests. Stalk cutting and disposal of plant parts normally left in fields following harvest is an example. Insects that live through the winter in such stalks and attack crops the following year are dramatically reduced by this practice. Some insects can be controlled in field crops by delaying the planting until the insects have passed through their most destructive stage of development.
6. *Hormone manipulation.* This practice can disrupt the life cycle of insects and limit the number that survive. Considerable research has been done with hormones that help regulate insect body functions. For example, the presence of juvenile hormones in an insect allows it to grow but not to mature. The absence of juvenile hormones allows a young insect to become an adult. If insects were to receive doses of juvenile hormones when

they would normally be maturing, development to the adult stage would not take place. Substances, similar to the juvenile and other hormones, have been found in some plants. These substances are being studied to determine their usefulness in the control of insects.

High hopes exist for alternatives to chemicals, but it appears that for the present we must depend on chemicals used selectively and prudently to control insect pests.

A guideline, resulting from recent experiences with insecticides, is that persistent substances should be released into the environment only when absolutely necessary. This means that DDT-like insecticides should be used only to protect human health or life-supporting food supplies and only under controlled conditions when no satisfactory alternative is available.

Suggestions for Further Reading

Journal Articles

1. Edwards, C. A. 1970. Persistent pesticides in the environment. Chemical Rubber Company.
2. Frost, J. 1969. Earth, air, water. *Environment* 11 (no. 6):14–33.
3. Holcolmb, R. W. 1970. Insect control: alternatives to the use of conventional pesticides. *Science* 168:456–58.
4. Irving, G. W., Jr. 1970. Agricultural pest control and the environment. *Science* 168:1419–24.
5. Keller, E. 1970. The DDT story. *Chemistry* 43:8–12.
6. Lykken, L. 1971. Chemical control of pests. *Chemistry* 44:18–21.
7. Shea, K. P. 1971. Old weapons are best. *Environment* 13 (no. 5):40–49.
8. Williams, C. M. 1967. Third-generation pesticides. *Scientific American* 2:1713–17.
9. Woodwell, G. M. 1967. Toxic substances and ecological cycles. *Scientific American* 216:24–31.
10. DDT substitutes. *Chemical and Engineering News* 49 (no. 31):7.

Government Documents

1. U.S. Dept. of Health, Education, and Welfare. 1969. *Report of the secretary's commission on pesticides and their relationship to environmental health*, parts I and II.
2. Executive Office of the President—Office of Science and Technology. 1971. *Ecological effects of pesticides on non-target species.*
3. U.S. Dept. of Agriculture. 1971. *Managing our environment.*

Chapter 13

Oil

Sources and Causes

During recent years the public has become increasingly aware of the presence of oil pollutants in the sea. Photographs and descriptions of oil-soaked birds floundering on oil-covered beaches have become almost routine presentations of the visual news media.

Oil pollution is an almost inevitable consequence of the dependence of a rapidly growing population on oil-based technology. The use of natural resources such as oil on a grand scale, without losses, is almost impossible. The extent of such losses, intentional or accidental, is steadily increasing and is becoming a great cause for concern.

It is estimated that the total oil influx into the ocean is between 5–10 million tons annually. The major sources are:

1. *Cargo tanker washings at sea.* The widespread practice of using sea water as ballast for empty tankers contributes an estimated 3 million tons of oil to the oceans annually. This takes place when the ballast is dumped and carries residual oil from the tanker into the sea.
2. *Bilge pumping at sea.* The dumping of bilge contents by ships other than tankers contributes an estimated 500,000 tons per year.
3. *In-port oil losses.* These losses occur during loading and unloading procedures and also as a result of collisions in port. The estimated annual contribution to oil pollution of the sea is 1 million tons.
4. *Other sources.* Some other sources are not easily assessed but do contribute to the problem. Vessel accidents on the high seas or near shore certainly add to the problem and receive great amounts of publicity. The largest spill to date in this category took place when the tanker *Torrey*

Canyon ran aground off the coast of England in March of 1967. The oil spill amounted to 100,000 tons.

Losses also occur during exploration for and production of oil. The blowout of wells, disposal of drilling muds and other wastes, and accidental damage to offshore drilling rigs all constitute significant potential pollution sources. The Santa Barbara spill of January, 1969, drew (through national headlines) the attention of the public to oil losses which can take place during production. In this case, the flow of oil continued unabated for eleven days despite efforts at containment.

Oil leakage from the 200,000 miles of pipeline that crosses waterways and reservoirs is a possible source of polluting oil. These lines are subject to cracks, punctures, corrosion, and other sources of damage which would lead to leaks.

It is estimated that nearly 2 million tons of used lubricating oil is unaccounted for each year in the United States alone. It is assumed that much of this eventually reaches coastal waters.

Table 13-1 shows the number of reported oil spills of 100 barrels or more that took place in U.S. waters during 1968 and 1969. Note that these figures reflect only the reported spills.

TABLE 13-1 REPORTED OIL SPILLS

SOURCE	NUMBER OF SPILLS 1968	NUMBER OF SPILLS 1969
Sea vessels	347	532
Shore facilities	295	331
Unidentified	72	144
Total	714	1007

Adapted from U.S. Dept. of the Interior, *Clean Water for the 70's*, p. 8.

The Fate of Spilled Oil

Oil and water don't mix: so we have been told. According to this old adage, it might be expected that spilled oil would just float around until it was washed ashore. This, however, is not the case. One gallon of oil will cover an area of four acres of water when completely spread out. During the time it is spreading, many changes take place in the oil. All oils, regardless of type, contain volatile components that evaporate readily. Within a few days, 25% of the volume of a typical oil spill is lost through evaporation. The remaining oil is subjected to emulsification processes which, in a sense, do cause oil and water to mix.

Two types of emulsions are formed. Oil-in-water emulsions result when small droplets of oil become dispersed in water and are stabilized by chemical interaction with the water at their surfaces. This process takes place especially well in turbulent seas. The resulting oil droplets are not dispersed on top of the water, but rather throughout the water. Some oil droplets, especially those weighted down by mineral particles, even reach the bottom.

Water-in-oil emulsions form when water droplets become enclosed in sheaths of oil. The emulsion is stabilized by interactions between the enclosed water droplets and various resinous and asphaltic materials found in most crude oil. This type of emulsion shows up as a floating, sticky, viscous mass that, on occasion, contains enough water to cause the total volume to be greater than that of the original oil.

Most oil that survives the emulsification processes is degraded by spontaneous photo-oxidation and oxidation by microorganisms. The microorganisms are the most powerful source of oil decomposition found in the sea.

By the end of three months at sea only about 15% of the original volume of an oil spill remains. This is in the form of black, tarry lumps of a dense asphaltic substance, and it is these lumps that frequently wash up on beaches.

When massive spills occur close to shore, sufficient time is not available for the process described above to affect the total amount of oil involved. Under such circumstances a thick sticky film of oil is deposited on any solid that comes in contact with the spill.

Biological and Physical Effects

The problem of oil pollution may be thought of in terms of short-term and long-term effects. The short-term effects are immediately obvious and are the ones that have received the most publicity. The long-term effects are only slowly becoming apparent and are currently the subject of much study.

Short-term effects fall into two categories, those caused by coating and asphyxiation, and those that result from oil's toxicity. The effects caused by coating and asphyxiation are:

1. *Reduction of light transmission.* Measurements have shown that ambient light intensity 2 meters below an oil slick was 90% lower than at the same depth in clear water. Photosynthesis by marine plant life may be hampered by extended periods of such conditions.
2. *Dissolved oxygen reduction.* Oil films retard the rate of oxygen uptake by water. Measurements have shown a significantly lower dissolved oxygen level in water beneath a slick than in clear water. The final effects of this have not been determined.
3. *Damage to water birds.* Swimming and diving birds become covered with oil. This causes their feathers to mat together, reducing their buoyancy and preventing flight. The insulative value of the feathers is also lost, and some birds quickly die of exposure in cold water. It has been estimated that 25,000 sea birds died as a result of the *Torrey Canyon* incident.

4. *Smothering.* The effects of oil on plant life along shorelines have become a matter of concern. Intertidal algae and lichens are known to have been killed by smothering coats of oil which washed ashore in some areas.

The toxic effects of oil result from some of the many compounds that make up this very complex mixture. These compounds vary widely in their molecular weights and structures.

Until recently, low-boiling saturated hydrocarbons were considered to be harmless to a marine environment. It has now been demonstrated that these substances, in low water concentrations, produce anaesthesia and narcosis in a wide variety of lower animals. Cell damage and death result in animals exposed to high concentrations. It is indicated that larvae and other young forms of marine life may be especially affected.

Low-boiling aromatic hydrocarbons are abundant in oil and represent its most dangerous fraction. Such compounds as benzene, toluene, and xylene are found in this fraction. These substances are acute poisons for man as well as for all other living things. Naphthalene and phenanthrene, also present in oil, are even more toxic to fish than the three compounds mentioned.

The aromatic compounds are more water-soluble than the saturated hydrocarbons. The aromatics can kill marine organisms by direct contact (with oil) or through contact with dilute solutions created when the compounds dissolve into the water from the oil. The effect of these compounds diminishes somewhat with time because they are volatile components of oil and evaporate.

Observations conducted on oil spills close to shore indicate that massive, immediate destruction of marine life occurs during the first few days after a spill. The species affected include a wide range of fish, shellfish, worms, crabs, and other invertebrates. Bottom-living fish and lobsters are killed and washed ashore. The toxicity is immediate and leads to death within minutes or hours after contact.

The long-term and especially low-concentration effects of oil components on living systems are not as apparent as short-term effects. Some possible areas of concern have been proposed and are being studied.

Many biological processes of importance to the survival of marine life and occupying key positions in their life processes are mediated by extremely low concentrations of chemical messengers in sea water. Marine predators, for example, are attracted to their prey by organic compounds present in the sea water at concentrations in the ppb range. Similar chemical attractions and repulsions play important roles in such processes as finding food, escaping from predators, locating habitats, and sexual attraction.

There is reason to believe that some compounds of polluting oil interfere with these processes by blocking the taste receptors of organisms or by mimicking the natural stimuli, which leads to false responses on the part of the organisms. High-boiling saturated and aromatic compounds are the ones likely to interfere in this way. Such interference could have disastrous effects on the survival of some marine species.

The fate of organic compounds which enter the marine food chain has been studied. Results indicate that hydrocarbons, once incorporated into a particular organism, are quite stable, regardless of their structure. There is also evidence that these compounds can pass through many members of the marine food chain without becoming altered. Such compounds are thus subject to food-chain amplification analogous to the situation found for heavy metals and pesticides.

The food chain eventually reaches marine organisms that are harvested for human consumption. This presents the possibility that the flavor of seafood might be negatively affected, or, much worse still, that potential long-term poisons might accumulate in food used for human consumption. This latter point is especially unnerving when it is considered that some of the high-boiling aromatic hydrocarbons involved are known or thought to be carcinogenic.

The food-chain amplification could also lead to situations in which marine life high on the chain would accumulate quantities of the compounds sufficient to destroy them.

Emulsified oil may reach the sea bottom, as mentioned before, especially if it is weighted down by mineral particles. Oil on the sea floor usually persists for long periods of time and can continue to damage bottom plants and animals. The destruction of these plants and animals reduces the cohesion of bottom sediments and accelerates their transport. Sediment movement is commonly observed following oil spills. Contaminated sediments may be spread over great distances under the influence of tide and wave action.

Recent reports suggest an additional environmental threat from oil pollution: the oil may serve as a concentration medium for other fat-soluble poisons such as pesticides. Dissolved in an oil film, these poisons might reach concentrations many times higher than those common in polluted water. These poisons could, in this way, reach susceptible organisms in concentrations much higher than they would normally encounter.

Countermeasures for Oil Pollution

The obvious solution to this problem is to prevent it from happening. Since the principal cause of oil spills is human error, much effort can and should be directed at prevention. An area where progress can be made in this direction is transportation, where improved navigational aids (both ship- and shore-based) and improved safety and hazard warning instrumentation could prove effective. Off-shore drilling operations need improvement. Some suggestions are the development of submerged pyramid-shaped canopies to cover the drill hole area and collect and trap any spills, the use of mechanical or pneumatic (air curtain) walls around the drill site, and the use of some form of physical encapsulation of the drill and drill hole.

Accidents will take place in spite of prevention methods, and preparations should be made to handle such events. This is especially crucial because accidents often result in massive amounts of oil being released into small areas. The areas of immediate concern in the event of a massive spill are containment of as much oil as possible at the scene of the spill, and countermeasures for any oil that escapes containment. At the present time, neither area is without numerous problems.

Some proposals for research into at-source prevention have been made. These include:

1. Development of techniques to instantaneously convert the contents of storage or transport tanks into a gelled and viscous material that will not easily flow through ruptured tank walls or which might form self-sealing plugs.
2. Development of new methods for quickly patching holes in tankers, pipelines, and so forth.
3. Development of improved and accelerated salvage techniques.
4. Development of rapid, mobile, off-loading techniques coupled with transportable (possibly inflatable) containers, all of which could be air-lifted to accident sites.

Until progress can be made in the areas of at-source prevention, other containment and countermeasures will have to be used. Improvement is needed in these areas as well since, as mentioned before, problems do exist with the present methods.

The containment of an oil spill of necessity involves the creation of some sort of barrier. Three types of barriers have been used or are in the developmental stage. They are floating booms, water bubble barriers, and chemical barriers.

Floating booms are in common use in harbors and areas where the transfer of petroleum products takes place. These booms are constructed of a tubular floating section, which is inflatable or is filled with some buoyant material. Some sort of weighted skirt is usually suspended below the floating section. These booms are used to encircle and contain spills until they can be removed.

The success of these devices depends upon the conditions under which they are used. They are most effective in calm water and when used on small spills. Most commercially available models are unsatisfactory in the open sea or in any rough water because they become difficult to anchor, and wave action carries the oil over and under the barrier. Larger, more bulky and more rigid booms overcome this problem, but they are more difficult to transport and set up.

In emergencies, makeshift booms have been used. Construction materials for these devices include inflated fire hose, linked railroad ties, and telephone poles. A considerable amount of development and improvement is necessary to make floating booms useful in the rough-water situations that often accompany (and sometimes cause) accidental spills at sea or in harbors.

Water bubble barriers are formed by releasing compressed air from a perforated, submerged piece of tubing. The air rises to the surface as a curtain of tiny bubbles. The resulting agitation prevents or at least inhibits the movement of oil films across the curtain. The barrier works as long as water current and wind do not overcome the forces set up by the compressed air. These barriers are quite new and, although totally impractical for the open sea, they are in use in some harbors. One distinct advantage is that they do not impede the movement of vessels.

Certain chemical additives are capable of gelling or even solidifying oil. If these could be applied effectively to the periphery of an oil slick, it is conceivable that a ring of gelled oil could serve as a containment barrier, possibly in very rough seas. Work along this line is still in the experimental and development phase.

The job of containment is much easier in harbors and protected waters than on the open sea, where high waves and anchoring still prevent effective use of barriers.

Whether or not containment of a spill is successful, the task of cleanup and removal must be accomplished. The rash of spills in recent years has allowed numerous cleanup methods to be tried with the hope of finding a "best" one. Apparently some methods are better than others, and, in fact, some should be avoided completely because of long-term effects. Indeed, some of the more obvious methods are among the least desirable.

Mechanical methods of cleanup are very satisfactory from two points of view. The oil is removed from the water and reclaimed for productive use. Mechanical removal involves the use of skimmers, which are attached to ships and which effectively skim the oil and a thin layer of water from the surface. The oil and water are allowed to separate in storage tanks within the ship, and the water is then pumped out.

All skimmers now in use work best in calm waters and on thick layers of oil. They are quite effective on oil slicks contained by floating booms. The present recovery rate of skimmers is between 10 and 50 barrels per hour, depending on the calmness of the water and the type of skimmer. In summary, skimming is an ideal method for use on small, contained spills, but it is beset with difficulties when used on large spills in open water.

Hydrocarbons are naturally degraded by marine microorganisms. Accelerated biological degradation, using these same microorganisms, might be applicable to those oil spills in the open sea which will not reach shore for several days. This technique would involve bacterial seeding and fertilization of the oil slicks. In order to assure complete degradation, sufficient time would be needed and all appropriate bacterial species would have to be used. These bacteria are highly selective, and no single species could degrade all components of the oil.

A number of problems accompany this technique. The main one is the severe oxygen requirement for the degradation process. The complete degradation of 1 gallon of crude oil requires all the dissolved oxygen in 320,000 gallons of air-saturated sea water. Therefore, the oxidation will be slow (and maybe the slick will reach shore) in areas where the oxygen content of the water is low (possibly from previous pollution). The degradation might cause additional damage to marine life by depleting the oxygen.

Combustion served as one of the earliest methods used to rid water of oil pollution. It is an attractive and inexpensive method for disposing of large amounts of oil. It is, of course, inadvisable in situations where the oil is close to shore or to structures that could be damaged.

Generally, burning is effective only if it can begin immediately after a spill. The lighter fractions of oil evaporate immediately after a spill, and the remaining oil has a higher ignition temperature and can be difficult to ignite. This factor, coupled with the ability of water to conduct heat away from the burning oil, has caused some attempts to be unsuccessful. Research is now aimed at developing "aids to combustion" in the form of wicks, catalysts, and supplementary fuels. Further developments in burning techniques may lead to methods very useful on large spills in the open sea. One drawback is that water pollution is converted to air pollution, since dense black smoke is generated. The residue after burning is a black solid that is easier to collect than the liquid oil.

Small amounts of oil may be removed by sorbents. Oil is soaked up by an absorbent and clings to the surface of particles of an adsorbent. Either type of sorbent can be used to remove oil from the surface of water. The use of such materials has the advantage of limiting the rate of slick spreading and facilitating cleanup. The disadvantages include problems of delivery and application of the materials, and collection and disposal of the oil-soaked products. Also, the method is prohibitive with extremely large slicks because of the amounts of materials involved.

Straw and sawdust have been used as sorbents. After becoming saturated with oil, they are removed and disposed of. Shredded polyurethane foam, an absorbent, is used and has the advantage that, when it is saturated, it can be removed and the oil can be squeezed out. The foam can then be reused. The recovered liquid is 80% oil, which can be recovered for use. A volume of 50 ft^3 of foam will reportedly soak up 1 ton of crude oil.

Sinking agents, in the form of sand, brickdust, cement, silicone mixtures, and fly ash, have been added to oil spills. The combination of oil and sinking agent is heavier than water, and the oil sinks. Some of the agents are chemically treated to increase their properties of being attracted to oil and rejected by water. In order to be most effective, the sinking agent should not release the oil back to the water environment. This has been a problem with some agents.

The French used large amounts of sinking agents on the oil slick from the *Torrey Canyon* incident. This removed the immediate problem of having the slick reach the shorelines.

It now appears, as a result of studies on long-term effects, such as those previously discussed, that physical sinking is one of the least desirable methods of treating oil spills. Sunken oil kills bottom-dwelling animals so rapidly that most mobile dwellers have insufficient time to move. Oysters, scallops, and lobsters are among the species affected. The oil may form a layer or "blanket" on the bottom and persist for long periods of time.

The bacterial degradation of sunken oil requires large amounts of oxygen. As a result, sediments loaded with oil may become anaerobic. One of the principles of geochemistry is that hydrocarbons in anaerobic sediments persist indefinitely. Anaerobic sediments are very slowly reworked and repopulated, so such sites might constitute sources of water pollution for a long time after the original spill.

Many materials are available that will emulsify oil in water. These products are known by a variety of names, such as emulsifiers, detergents, degreasers, and dispersants. We shall use the term *dispersant.* The primary components of a dispersant are a surfactant, a solvent, and stabilizers. The surfactant has an affinity for both oil and water and allows the two to mix. Solvents enable the surfactant to penetrate into the oil slick. The solvent usually makes up the bulk of the dispersant composition. Stabilizers fix the emulsion once it is formed. The net effect of the dispersant is to lower the surface tension of the oil to the point where it will break up and disperse in the water in the form of tiny droplets.

The action of dispersants increases the surface area of an oil slick and distributes the oil droplets into a large volume of water. These two effects enhance the natural degradation by microorganisms. The chemical dispersants themselves do not destroy any oil.

Dispersants are usually applied by spraying. Agitation is necessary to make them effective. This makes them very useful on oil slicks in rough open sea where nature does the agitating. Evaluation of the results of their use in the past indicates that dispersants should be used with caution. The high degree of dispersion they create leads to greater solubility and higher concentrations of oil in the water than would be possible if natural dispersion were allowed to take place. Also, the oil droplets formed are in a size range that is easily ingested and assimilated by marine organisms on the low end of the marine food chain. In the case of the *Torrey Canyon* incident, some of the dispersants used were found to be as toxic to aquatic life as the oil itself.

Dispersants used on beaches actually add to the problem by causing the oil to penetrate more deeply into the sand. The compactness of the sand is upset, and it becomes more easily moved by tide and wave action. This contributes to beach erosion.

Suggestions for Further Reading

Journal Articles

1. Blumer, M. 1971. Scientific aspects of the oil spill problem. *Environmental Affairs* 1:54–73.
2. Oil spill technology makes strides. 1971. *Environmental Science and Technology* 5:674–75.

Government Documents

1. American Petroleum Institute. 1969. A primer on oil spill clean-up. In *Water pollution—1969,* part 4. Hearings before Committee on Public Works, U.S. Senate, 91st Congress, 1st session, pp. 1248–60.
2. Environmental Protection Agency. 1970. *Effects of oil pollution on waterfowl: a study of salvage methods.* Water Population Control Research Series, 15080.

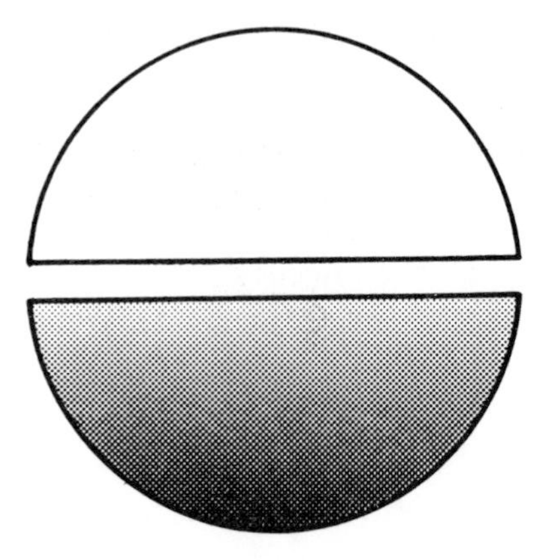

Chapter 14

Waste Water Treatment

Introduction

A total of 2,615 billion gallons of water is used daily in the United States. This is more than 6 times the average daily flow of the Mississippi River. Most of this amount, 2,300 billion gallons (about ⅞ of the total), is used to generate hydroelectric power. Water put to this use is returned to streams and rivers virtually unchanged and available for further use.

The other 315 billion gallons per day (bgd) is the cause for much concern, for this is the water which, through use, becomes filled with various pollutants. The four main areas of use for this 315 bgd are:

1. Industry (177 bgd)
2. Irrigation (120 bgd)
3. Public supply (16 bgd)
4. Rural supply, domestic and livestock (2 bgd)

The quality of water is changed (lowered) by use in each of these categories. The change is drastic in some instances.

Most water used in the above areas is returned to the general water supply after use: this presents a problem because of the increasing number of pollutants being found in used water. The question of what happens to these pollutants in our water supply is being asked more and more frequently.

The purpose of this chapter is to discuss waste water treatment with particular attention devoted to substances that are and are not removed from waste water and the physical and chemical processes by which they are removed.

The most common form of water pollution control in the U.S. consists of a system of sewers and waste water treatment plants. Waste water is collected by the sewer system and delivered to the waste treatment plant, where it is made "fit" for discharge back into the general water supply. The discovery of more pollutants is causing serious questions to be raised concerning the real meaning of the term "fit" as used above.

Three categories of waste water treatment processes presently exist: primary, secondary, and tertiary or advanced.

Primary Treatment Process

Primary treatment consists of separating the water from solid matter by letting the solids settle or by removing any floating scum. This operation is normally carried out in a series of steps.

1. *Screening.* Large floating objects are removed by passing the waste water through screens. Some plants use a device called a comminutor, which screens and grinds the material. The shredded or ground material remains in the water to be removed later in a settling tank.
2. *Grit removal.* Sand, grit, cinders, and small stones are allowed to settle to the bottom of a grit chamber. This is a very important step for cities that have combined storm and municipal sewage systems. The grit obtained in this process is disposed of by using it for land fill.
3. *Sediment removal.* Sewage, even after removal of grit, still contains suspended solids. These will settle out if the speed of sewage flow is reduced. This is accomplished in a sedimentation tank. The suspended solids settle out and the solid mass, called raw sludge, is collected for disposal.

The primary treatment is completed when the effluent, from which grit and sludge have been removed, is treated with chlorine gas before discharge

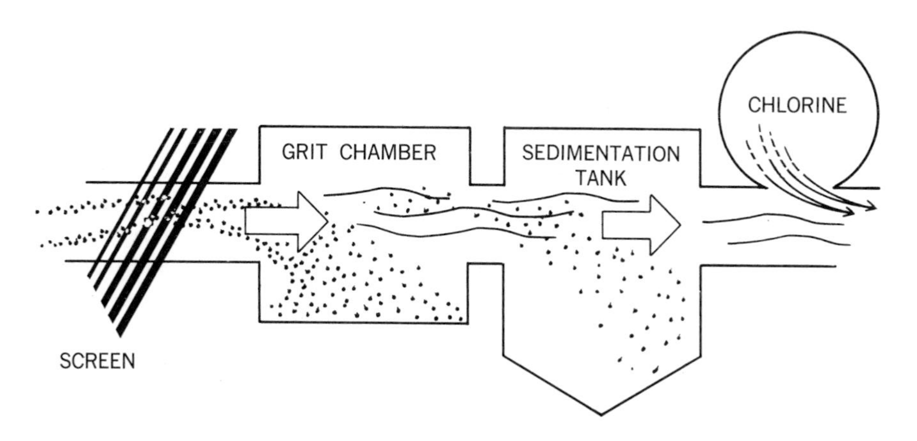

FIGURE 14-1 PRIMARY SEWAGE TREATMENT

Redrawn from U.S. Dept. of the Interior, *A Primer on Waste Water Treatment*, p. 4.

into a stream or river. Chlorine gas is added to destroy disease-causing bacteria. All of the steps in primary treatment of sewage are represented in Fig. 14-1.

Primary treatment removes about one-third of the BOD and suspended solids and a few percent of the refractory (persistent) organic compounds and plant nutrients. It is obvious that today, when concentrations of pollutants are discussed in parts per million, simple primary treatment of sewage should be supplemented by further treatment methods. It is a fact, however, that sewage from a little less than one-fourth of the U.S. population receives only primary treatment. Worse still, sewage from about 5% receives no treatment at all. Nearly one-third of the population lives in areas not served by sewer systems, and sewage is discharged into septic tanks or lagoons.

Secondary Treatment Process

Sewage from about 40% of the population receives secondary as well as primary treatment. Two processes are currently available for secondary treatment: the trickling filter and activated sludge processes.

An efficiently operating activated sludge system can remove up to 90% of the suspended solids and BOD. A good trickling filter system is capable of removing 80–85%, but in practice 75% is more common.

A trickling filter is simply a bed of stones and gravel 3 to 10 feet deep, through which the sewage passes slowly. Bacteria gather and multiply on the stones and gravel until they become numerous enough to consume most of the organic matter in the sewage. The water, after passing through the activated bed, trickles out through pipes in the bottom of the filter.

The trend in new secondary treatment plants is away from trickling filters and toward the activated sludge process. In this process, the rate of bacterial action is increased by bringing air and bacteria-laden sludge into very intimate contact with the sewage, which has previously received primary treatment. The essentials of the process are illustrated in Fig. 14-2. Sewage, air, and activated sludge remain in contact for several hours in the aeration tank. During this time, the organic wastes are broken down by bacterial action.

A recent improvement in the process has been made by using pure oxygen instead of air. It has been known for a number of years that more bacteria could be supported in a smaller space with less pumping of air (oxygen) if pure oxygen were used. An economically competitive system using oxygen has only recently been developed. The system achieves 90% utilization of oxygen, compared to 5–10% in conventional systems. This has been called by some the most significant recent advance in sewage treatment.

The sewage flows from the aeration tank into another sedimentation tank, where solids are removed. Chlorination completes the basic secondary treatment.

The sludge, which contains the bacteria, can be used again by returning it to the aeration tank and mixing it with new sewage and air or pure oxygen.

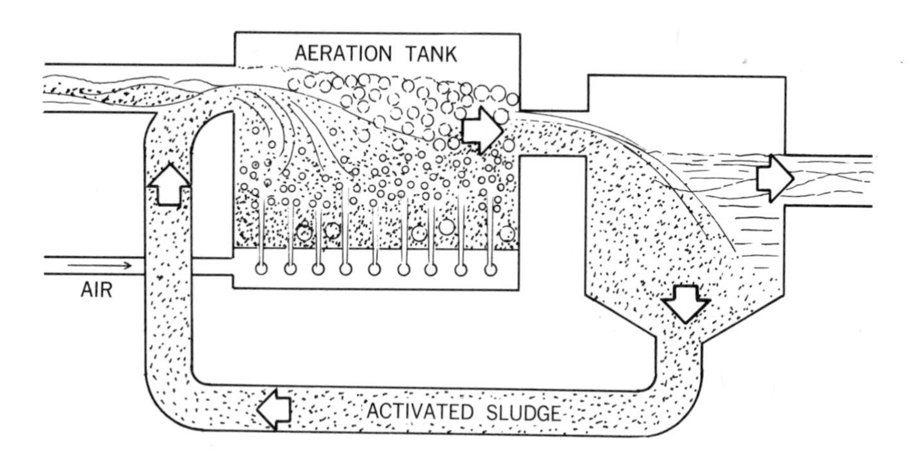

FIGURE 14-2 ACTIVATED SLUDGE PROCESS
Redrawn from U.S. Dept. of the Interior, *A Primer on Waste Water Treatment*, p. 5.

Tertiary or Advanced Treatment Processes

Primary and secondary sewage treatment lower the BOD of the water and eliminate harmful bacteria. They do not, however, effectively remove other dissolved organic and inorganic compounds. If water is going to meet water quality standards of the federal government (some are now in effect and others are yet to be established), attention must be paid to these modern-day pollutants.

Thousands of waste treatment plants will be constructed or expanded in the future to meet the demands for pure water, and these plants will be built to meet the government's water quality standards. They will look and operate much differently from the plants built during the last 30 years.

During the last decade a wide variety of treatment steps beyond secondary have been considered, and some are now being incorporated into water treatment sequences on a trial basis. These advanced treatment techniques, under investigation, range from extensions of biological processes capable of removing nitrogen and phosphorus nutrients, to physico-chemical separation techniques such as adsorption, distillation, and reverse osmosis.

Most dissolved refractory organic compounds remain in water that has gone through primary and secondary treatment. These persistent compounds resist bacterial action. The effects of such compounds in water are not all known, but taste and odor problems, tainting of edible fish, and fish kills have been attributed to their presence.

It has been found possible to remove 70–80% of these compounds by passing the previously treated water through a bed of activated carbon. The organic compounds leave the water and are adsorbed on the surface of the carbon. Most of the carbon now used is in granular form, but the use of a powdered form is being investigated. The powdered form requires less contact time but is more difficult to handle. Granular carbon can be reactivated for further use by heating it in multiple hearth furnaces. A loss of about 5% of the carbon is experienced during each reactivation.

When powdered carbon is used, it is put directly into the water. The organics adsorb to the carbon, which is then removed by using coagulating chemicals. The usefulness of the process depends upon the development of effective methods for regenerating the used powdered carbon for re-use.

The plant nutrient, phosphorus, can be removed from water by precipitation methods. This technique may be used as a separate step in waste water treatment. Two chemical approaches are commonly used: in one, lime (CaO) if added to make the water alkaline and to precipitate the phosphorus; and in the other approach, metallic hydroxides are added. In either case, the inorganic phosphorus (as phosphate) is precipitated as insoluble phosphate salts of such metal cations as Fe^{+3}, Al^{+3} or Ca^{+2}, and the organic phosphorus compounds are adsorbed onto the hydroxide floc (precipitate) formed by these same cations in alkaline solutions. The resulting sludge can be collected and treated to regenerate the precipitating agent.

Unfortunately, nitrates, the other basic plant nutrient, cannot be removed the same way as phosphates because most nitrates are water-soluble. Biological methods are being sought as possible solutions to this problem.

The removal of inorganic salts is a problem which must be dealt with in water treatment. Typically, a city doubles the initial concentration of salts in water by using it. A possible method for removing these salts from used water is electrodialysis. Electricity and membranes are used in this complicated process. The membrane used is usually made of some chemically treated plastic.

When this method is used, an electric current is passed through the water by means of two electrodes. The immersed electrodes are separated from each other by membranes. The ions in solution are attracted toward the electrodes, pass through the membranes, and leave cleaner water behind. The treated water is ready for re-use or further treatment. A typical cell used in this process is represented in Fig. 14-3.

The electrodialysis method has two problems associated with it. Organic molecules cannot be removed by the process and tend to collect on the membranes and reduce the effectiveness of the cell. The second problem is that of finding suitable disposal sites for the large amounts of brackish waste water produced. Because of the latter problem, the process may be limited to use in areas located near large bodies of salt water, where disposal is possible.

A one-step electrodialysis treatment of water, with units now being tested, reduces the total dissolved salt content by about 35% and allows a 92% recovery of water. A reduction of salt content by 35% is significant, since it represents an amount of dissolved salts nearly equal to that added by a typical city as a result of use. Thus, the salts added to sewage during use in a city can nearly all be removed before the sewage is returned to the general supply.

A process known as osmosis takes place when two solutions of different concentration are separated from each other by a permeable membrane. During this process, water molecules flow from the less concentrated solution,

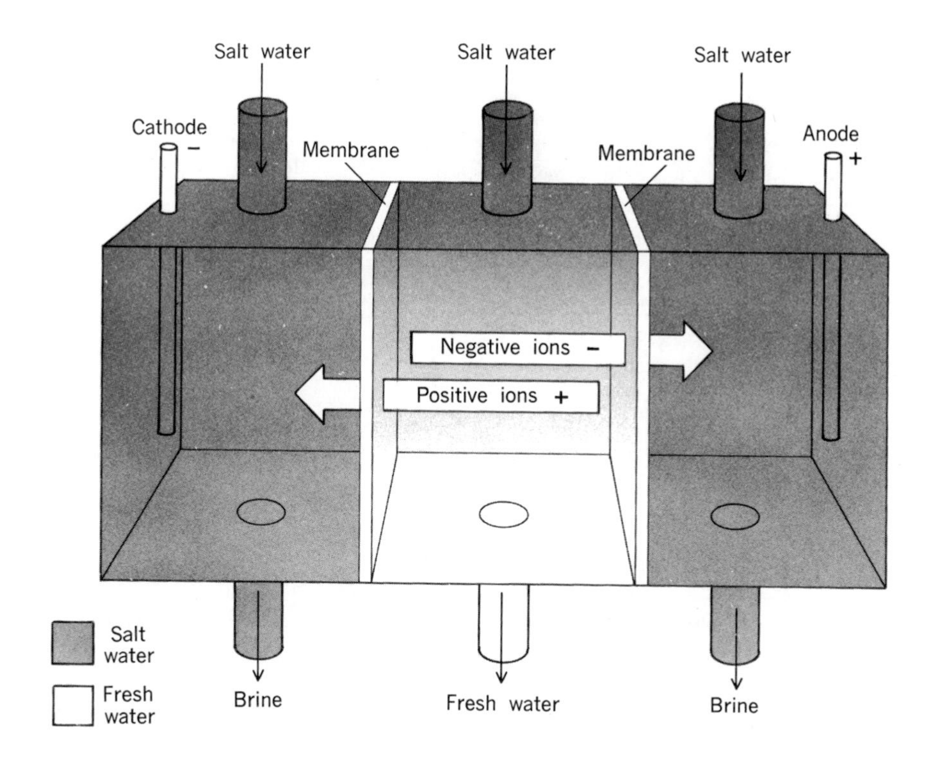

FIGURE 14-3 ELECTRODIALYSIS CELL

Redrawn from Richard H. Wagner, *Environment and Man* (New York: W. W. Norton and Co., Inc., 1971), p. 102.

through the membrane, into the more concentrated solution, until both concentrations are equal.

Reverse osmosis uses the above naturally-occurring process in reverse. Sufficient pressure can be exerted on the solution of higher concentration to overcome the tendency for water molecules to flow in, and instead cause them to flow out. This process amounts to removing water from the waste materials, rather than removing the waste materials from water. A diagram of this process appears in Fig. 14-4 (see following page).

One of the problems encountered with this equipment is devising a suitable support for the large surfaces of the weak membrane so it can withstand the necessary pressure. Organic molecules tend to foul the membrane, but the problem is not as serious with this technique as it is in electrodialysis.

Since it is the water and not the ions that pass through the membrane, reverse osmosis can reduce both organic and mineral salt content of the water. Pilot plant studies show a 90% reduction of total solids and a 75% recovery of water. The disposal of brackish water is a problem with this method, as it is with electrodialysis.

It must be noted that none of the processes discussed can complete the job of water treatment alone. They must be used in some sort of series with

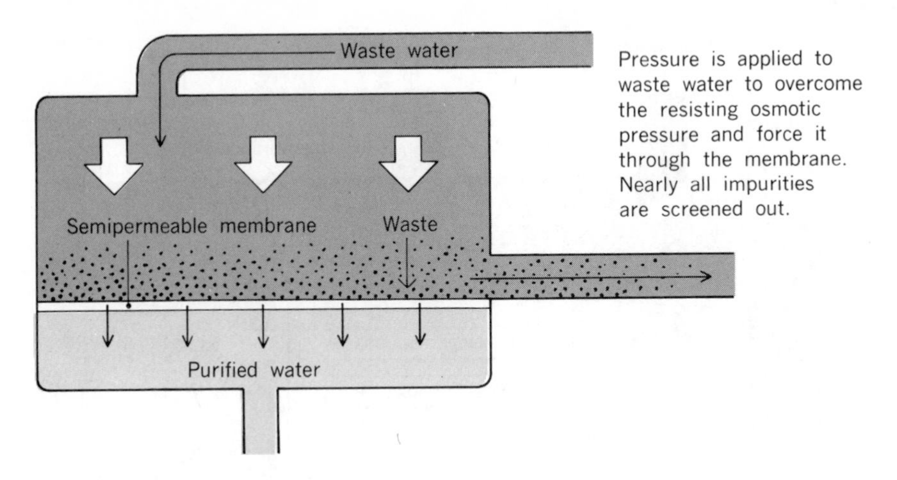
Waste water
Pressure is applied to waste water to overcome the resisting osmotic pressure and force it through the membrane. Nearly all impurities are screened out.
Semipermeable membrane
Waste
Purified water

FIGURE 14-4 REVERSE OSMOSIS

Redrawn from *Science Year 1971* (Chicago: Field Enterprises Educational Corporation, 1971), p. 141.

primary and secondary treatment methods. A series of treatment steps that might be applied, for example, is:

1. *Primary treatment*. Removes material that will settle or float.
2. *Secondary treatment*. Removes biologically decomposable impurities.
3. *Precipitation*. Removes phosphorus compounds and suspended solids.
4. *Adsorption*. Removes dissolved organics.
5. *Electrodialysis*. Returns dissolved salt concentration to the level present before use.
6. *Chlorination*. Removes disease-causing organisms.

A series of steps such as these does show promise for waste water treatment in the future.

Suggestions for Further Reading

Journal Articles

1. Holcolmb, R. W. 1970. Waste-water treatment: the tide is turning. *Science* 169:457–59.
2. Sludge handling: the hardest phase of waste treatment. 1971. *Environmental Science and Technology* 5:670–71.

Government Documents

1. U.S. Dept. of the Interior. 1969. *A primer on waste water treatment.* Federal Water Pollution Control Administration.

Index

Air, normal composition, 2–3
Air pollutants
  categories, 4
  emission figures, 4, 11, 28, 41, 54, 69
  relative toxicities, 5
  sources, 4–5, 10–12, 27–28, 40–41, 53–55, 68–70
  units of measurement, 6
  weighted mass of, 5–6
Asbestos, detrimental effects, 75–76
Automobile
  exhaust reactors for, 19–22, 35–36, 50–51
  federal emission standards for, 19–20
  use of alternate fuels, 23
  use of leaded vs. nonleaded gasoline, 21–23

Beryllium, detrimental effects, 73–75
Biochemical Oxygen Demand (BOD)
  determination of, 92–93
  levels, 93–94

Carbon dioxide, and the greenhouse effect, 84–88
Carbon monoxide
  atmospheric concentrations, 13–16
  atmospheric fate, 12–13
  detrimental effects, 16–19
  emission control methods, 19–24
  formation, 8–10
  sources, 10–12

DDT
  detrimental effects, 159–165
  evaluation of effects, 159–160
  history, 157–158
  solutions to problems involving, 164–167
Detergents
  biodegradability, 144–145
  chemical formulation, 142–144
  definition, 142
  detrimental effects, 144–145
  effects of phosphate removal, 148–150
  phosphate vs. nonphosphate, 145–147
Disease-causing agents
  and Coliform bacteria, 95–96
  examples, 95
Dissolved oxygen (DO). *See* Oxygen

Eutrophication, definition, 96–97

Greenhouse effect
  detrimental effects, 86–88
  role of CO_2, 84–88

Heat. *See* Thermal pollution
Hydrocarbons
  and the photolytic cycle, 41–43
  atmospheric concentrations, 39
  classes, 38
  detrimental effects, 46–49
  emission control methods, 49–51
  sources, 40–41

Inorganic chemicals, detrimental effects, 101–106
Insecticides
  alternatives, 165–167
  classes, 153–154
  degradation, 156
  toxicities, 154–155

Lead
  behavior in the body, 139–140
  detrimental effects, 136–140
  in gasoline, 21–23, 134–136
  pollution sources, 133–138
  properties and uses, 131–133

Mercury
  biological amplification, 124–126
  detrimental effects, 124–128
  methylation of, 126–128
  pollution sources, 123
  properties and uses, 119–121
Metals. *See* Trace metals

Nitrogen oxides
  and the photolytic cycle, 28–30
  atmospheric concentrations, 30–31
  atmospheric fate, 31–32
  detrimental effects, 32–34
  emission control methods, 34–36
  formation, 25–27
  sources, 27–28
NO_2 photolytic cycle. *See* Photolytic cycle
Nuclear power plants
  location, 111
  operation, 110–112
  wastes, 112–113

Oil
  amount produced, 101
  detrimental effects, 170–172
  fate of spilled, 169–170
Oil pollution
  countermeasures, 172–176
  sources, 168–169

Oxidants. *See* Photochemical oxidants
Oxygen, normal water concentrations, 92
Oxygen-demanding wastes
  decomposition of, 92–94
  detrimental effects, 91–94
  types, 92
Ozone. *See* Photochemical oxidants

Particulates
  atmospheric concentrations, 70–71
  detrimental effects, 71–79
  emission control methods, 80–82
  physical properties, 66–68
  sources, 68–70
Peroxyacylnitrates (PAN). *See* Photochemical oxidants
Phosphates
  in detergent formulation, 142–144
  problems in detergents, 144–145
  removal from detergents, 145–150
Photochemical oxidants
  atmospheric concentrations, 43–44
  detrimental effects, 45–49
  formation, 40–43
  important types, 39–40
Photochemical smog, mode of formation, 41–42
Photolytic cycle
  involvement of hydrocarbons, 41–43
  involvement of NO_x, 28–30
  unbalancing of, 41–43
Plant nutrients
  and eutrophication, 96–97
  determination of limiting, 98–100
  detrimental effects, 97

Radioactive wastes, sources, 108–113

Sediments
  detrimental effects, 106–108
  rates of sedimentation, 106–107
Smog. *See* Photochemical smog
Sulfur oxides
  atmospheric concentrations, 55–56
  detrimental effects, 57–62
  emission control methods, 62–64
  mode of formation, 52–53
  sources, 53–55
Synthetic organic chemicals
  production, 100
  types, 100

Temperature inversion
  definition, 83–85
  detrimental effects, 83–85
Thermal pollution
  detrimental effects, 114–116
  sources, 113–114
Trace metals, detrimental effects, 74

Waste water treatment
  primary, 179–180
  secondary, 180
  tertiary, 181–183
Water
  acidity effects, 103
  control of acidity, 102
  criteria for purity, 90–91
  deoxygenation effects, 92–94
  salinity effects, 104–106
  sources of acidity, 101
  sources of salinity, 103–104
Water pollutants, categories, 90
Water treatment plants. *See* Waste water treatment

3 4 5 6 7 8 9 10 11 12 13 14 15 16 17 18 19 20 21 22 23 24 25 80 79 78 77 76 75 74 73